To Lee

Christmas

G000141741

WHERE I USED TO PLAY
ON THE GREEN

WHERE I USED TO PLAY ON THE GREEN

A Novel

by

GLYN HUGHES

LONDON
VICTOR GOLLANCZ LTD
1982

© Glyn Hughes 1982
First published January 1982
Second impression November 1982

British Library Cataloguing in Publication Data
Hughes, Glyn
  Where I used to play on the green.
  I. Title
  823'.914[F]   PR605.U35
  ISBN 0-575-02997-8

Printed in Great Britain by
St Edmundsbury Press
Bury St Edmunds, Suffolk

I went to the Garden of Love,
And saw what I never had seen:
A Chapel was built in the midst,
Where I used to play on the green.

And the gates of this Chapel were shut,
And "Thou shalt not" writ over the door;
So I turn'd to the Garden of Love
That so many sweet flowers bore;

And I saw it was filled with graves,
And tomb-stones where flowers should be;
And Priests in black gowns were walking their rounds,
And binding with briars my joys and desires.

WILLIAM BLAKE, "Songs of Experience" 1793

Acknowledgements

The writing of this book has been greatly assisted by the Arts Council of Great Britain, with a bursary and a fellowship at Bishop Grosseteste College, Lincoln, during 1979–81. I must thank Alan Sillitoe, who supported my application, also the College Principal, Leonard Marsh, the governors and those of the staff who have welcomed me and offered their facilities in Lincoln.

My novel owes a general debt of inspiration to several recent historians, such as Christopher Hill and Raymond Williams and especially to E. P. Thompson's classic *The Making of The English Working Class*. My attitude to the Methodists owes much to his scholarship. What I have learnt has passed into unconscious levels and been transformed in this novel, so no doubt my book is littered with debts which it is impossible to specify. For one thing, Thompson and others have led me to a number of primary sources in which I discovered characters who have stimulated me. One such incident is my description of the Haworth Union Society, which owes something to E. P. Thompson.

There have been several biographies of Grimshaw from the late eighteenth century onwards. The only thoroughly researched one is Frank Baker's *William Grimshaw* (Epworth Press, 1963). Whilst Mr Baker will probably want to dissociate his view of Grimshaw from mine, he has been good enough to discuss the central character of my novel with me and his work has been of great value in creating my own more licensed portrait. I recommend anyone who wants a more factual "life" to turn to Frank Baker's book.

Finally, I am grateful for the editorial assistance I have received from my publishers — particularly Heather Todd, who has come up with many suggestions. And to Roya my wife, who helped throughout and typed the script.

Chapter 1

APRIL 1733 IN the West Riding of Yorkshire. The wastes of peat on the hills had a grey clammy look of the cooled and sodden ashes of the forests that had been burnt there. The moors now stretched across the landscape softly, like blown breath. New quarries of golden stone scarred the hills. New weavers' cottages, with rows of white cloth glittering in wooden frames called "tenters" where they were put to dry in the enclosures, were scattered over the slopes to make use of the water trickling out of the sodden moors and carefully channelled down stone gutters so as not to waste a drop. On the hilltops there was still some snow, but the valleys were full of trees coming into bud, of grass and flowers — primroses, dandelions and camomile. Because spring had arrived, the packhorse tracks were busy — with the clothiers' strings of Galloway ponies (a bandy-legged breed from carrying heavy bales of cloth), with weavers, often walking with their pieces of weaving on their heads, pedlars and merchants come sniffing out a new prosperity in the north, and colliers drifting about the hilltop pits. There were huddles of people in graveyards because the winter had as usual decimated most poor families. Beggars, discharged soldiers, herb-gatherers and tribes of poor people scoured the countryside, grazing on mushrooms and cresses. A bored child plucked a bunch of useless small flowers and waved it whilst she stared at a fabulous, old-fashioned, trundling coach.

Two young ladies, Sarah and Mary Lockwood, were travelling in the carriage. It also held William Grimshaw, the cheerful and beefy young curate of Todmorden. Like an ox in a luscious meadow he gained quiet satisfaction from contemplating man's conquest of this harsh region, with enclosures and the weaving industry. He was twenty-five years of age, five feet ten inches tall, and he seemed to fill the musty leather womb of the coach — he was one of those men who always appear to fill up the whole space around them even if it's the size of a church. He had quite recently left Cambridge, which place had not cured him of his native Lancashire accent. The Lockwoods had not met Grimshaw before an hour ago when he rose out of a peat gully where he had been hiding to shoot at moor fowl and helped them to move their vehicle that had got stuck in a snow-drift. There had been something very crow-like about him stooped in the gully, crouching for the rise as a crow first sinks its heavy blue-black shoulders before springing powerfully into flight. The coachman seemed puny and overpowered by the parson who put his shoulder to the wheel, screwing up his face as if to squeeze blood out of it. (There was a strong and manly temper lurking behind that expression, Sarah thought.) Afterwards the curate stood carelessly, not at all like a gentleman, dripping sweat, his clothes loose, breathing heavily and quite asthmatically. He hauled into the carriage a fashionable gun and a bundle of bloody feathers, and he gave off an outdoor smell of game, gunpowder and man-sweat. Sarah and Mary Lockwood (who held bunches of primroses, in most genteel postures because of their passenger) struggled not to show their alarm at his unrefined features, which were so much more like those of an engineer or a merchant than of a Bachelor of Arts. As a clergyman he was obviously more fitting for rough Yorkshire weavers and clothiers than for a southern university. At the same time they noticed how his plump cheeks came forwards in the softer sensuality of a Cupid's bow — his lips looked as innocently eager to kiss or to suck as a child's are.

The Lockwood sisters were daughters of a wealthy clothier, John Lockwood of Mytholmroyd. It kept them rather lonely, being unwanted as company by the lower class of weavers, farmers and artisans, and also by the traditional aristocracy who despised tradesmen. The desire for amusement glittered in the eyes of both ladies. As they jolted by the wealthier houses — many of which were encased in scaffolding, or showed other signs of re-fashioning — Sarah and Mary chattered about Christmas balls and visitors from London or the continent, suggesting exaggerated intimacy with their father's rivals.

"Ours is not a genial place, Mr Grimshaw," Mary Lockwood said. "Our moors put you in fear o' being stabbed in the back! We are without cultivation except for kicking one another to death in clog fights o' the long dark winter nights. This is a godless place, dark and inhospitable."

"But profitable," Grimshaw remarked. "And the hunting is good." He stroked his bundles of blood-stained feathers.

8

Mary was surprised at a clergyman who did not take up her reference to godlessness but spoke of profit instead. "We are enjoying many improvements and the building of moorland enclosures," she said. "The pity is that it unsettles the poor so that it is difficult to obtain servants — everyone now expects to get rich without working for it."

"I love the moors, with all their faults," Sarah contributed. "I think they are beautiful."

"But surely you agree with your sister that there *is* something murderous here? A man will go home and kill his wife out of sheer desperation or for something to occupy him. The place seems to have an evil demon lurking in it."

"The demons are in the hearts and minds of those who look upon it," Sarah said. She felt his eyes resting with impertinent steadfastness upon her, so she hid behind a handkerchief which, the curate noticed, was bloodstained. He also observed that she coughed in the manner of those who do so habitually; that her chest was weak, her bones slender; and that she had the vanity, or the delicacy, to hide her sinewy neck with a high collar — an attention to appearances not shared by her sister! William guessed that if Sarah loosed her long fair hair it would be luxuriant, as it often is with sickly people. She seemed constantly ready for laughter. You could detect it behind her every expression, the corners of her mouth twitched with it and it lurked in her watchful eyes — a Lancashire characteristic rather than a Yorkshire one, William thought. At a place where carters were arguing about their rights of passage over a bridge, the more dour and shrewd sister, Mary, drew out of her cloak what she said was syrup of horehound, and she told William to take it for his heavy breathing.

Before they reached Todmorden, Grimshaw amused his companions with his favourite story about how his ancestors had killed a dragon in a wood near Blackburn. He described the fearful movement in the grass, the damp shiny scales, the tongue spitting bubbles of saliva like mercury melted in the fire of its breath, the menacing coils — a snake as hideous as that first serpent cast out of Heaven and which became Satan. The Grimshaw family had later — oh, much later, when the incident had become a distant memory — put a serpent on their coat of arms, to mark how they had made it possible for maidens to walk safely in the woods. William Grimshaw was very conscious of dragons, in one form or another. Just as serpents

9

lurked in the woods and the waters, so the wicked natures with which we were born, no matter how well they were disciplined, waited always to trap or misguide us. Thus for instance we were tempted into Popery, that abomination! William had been brought up a Protestant in Brindle, a Catholic district of north-west Lancashire which was the most southerly stronghold of the Scottish papists in their 1715 rebellion, and the Protestants had feared that the clock would be put back to a new Dark Age with cruelty, licentiousness, profligacy, superstition and louse-ridden Scotsmen everywhere. William was seven years old at the time and he grew up vaguely associating their Virgin and her sensual melancholy with forbidden things.

As William stepped down at Todmorden, Sarah plucked a stray woodcock feather off her dress — the carriage was full of feathers — balanced it on her palm and blew it like a kiss out of the window. Over the landscape, steam was rising from the thawing snow. A strong smell of sweat rose from the horses, twitching restlessly because the spring had already hatched a few flies. As the curate squared up to the narrow Todmorden streets, where looms clattered before the windows of upper rooms, where women were enjoying the sunshine by bringing their spinning wheels onto their doorsteps and where everyone noticed that Grimshaw was passing by, his every movement spoke his confidence in being able to make his mark on earth, even if he never reached Heaven. And yet at this point Sarah realised — as people did at their second impression — that Grimshaw was not quite as big as she'd imagined. The impact of his temperament was the largest thing about him. And the coachman, who seemed to be concentrating on the horses' ears, was in fact wondering what it was like to have such a wild young man as your parson. The coach rattled on its way, everyone in it and on it thinking about Parson Grimshaw.

A short time later William was invited to the Lockwoods' home for a further supply of Mary's medicine. The master clothier's mansion at Mytholmroyd — five miles from Todmorden down the Calder Valley towards Halifax — had originally been a farmhouse called "Ellis Gate" (or "Yate" as it was pronounced) which was renamed "Ewood Court", and surrounded with dye works, sizing house, fulling mill and barns. The gable ends were as broad as the bums of well-fed clothiers. Under the eaves and over the window sills were carvings of crouching dogs, ugly old women, serpents and dragons. A Grimshaw had killed a dragon; these Lockwoods had turned it to stone and mounted it on their house.

William Grimshaw arrived as usual on foot and muddy. From the entrance hall he glimpsed Sarah playing the spinet. Music meant little to him — even church music seemed to him a mere decoration of the liturgy. Sarah's tinkling sounded to him like the pleasant flashing of a stream on a summer's day: mere surface; but what interested him was to catch and eat the fat trout hidden in the depths. Without paying attention to the sounds she was making, Grimshaw greedily watched the movements of her back and shoulders, her fingers and wrists, her hair, the gown stirring on her hips.

John Lockwood came to meet him. He was sixty years old, strong and thick-wristed. His chest and shoulders were broad, he had a heavy stomach and he was full of gravity — he was built like his own fat barns. The parson and the clothier glared smiles at one another; their teeth were like rows of armour in defence of their thoughts. Both men talked loudly, used to and enjoying a constant flutter of apprehension in the household and servants surrounding them — as occurred during their first conversation. Lockwood was delighted by Grimshaw's worldly knowledge, especially of the laws of land and property. Still, Lockwood kept his fists clenched, tight and ungenerous, as was his habit, whilst he boasted. "Twenty thousand pounds' worth of my low-priced kersey cloths are exported every year to the hospitals, common soldiers and poorer folk of Europe, Russia and Turkey, Mr Grimshaw! I also make some finer woollens named after my daughters — Sarah Lockwood, a bird's-eye, and Mary Lockwood, a worsted. The ladies of Saint Petersburg are delighted with them! I import timber from Russia, and supply the officers of their Court with the finest woollens. The soldiers of Holland, too. And Spain! They consume a lot o' beautiful cloth in their wars. When they've done with it and left it miry and gored on the battlefields we still have some use of our customers because we bring their bones to Yorkshire to fertilise my enclosures. The battlefields of the continent are full of useless bones. I am an ordinary man out to do no more than make an honest living. The folk at the Cloth Hall still call me 'John O'Jack O'Bill O't Yate' and I do not find argument and disputation profitable; nonetheless God's Grace falls into my lap. By the Grace of God I can dine off silver and pewter, even though for the most part I choose to live modestly and use wooden

11

platters. It seems to me that God in this part of the country discourages excess and rewards trade — I don't know what happens in the south, for I find them less God-fearing down there; I often go to Norwich and Bristol for wool. My daughters have good dowries and I would like to see them married. I am a widower, Mr Grimshaw, and have neither sons nor grandsons. My girls have practical natures . . .''

By "practical natures" Lockwood, in his peculiar dry speech that made you wonder whether he was laughing at you or not, alluded euphemistically to the private passions of his outcast daughters. Sarah wandered the moors, on horseback or even more dangerously on foot, dreaming, brooding, useless, even for a while trying to read books (although she had never been taught and had thankfully given that up), coming home often soaked with rain, coughing and sweating fearfully — people said she was crazed by the deaths of her husbands, for at the age of twenty-three she had gone through two of them, "like colic through a horse" as John Lockwood put it. The unmarried Mary meanwhile brewed herbs and potions instead of looking for a husband. Ewood Court stank of the plants which the kitchen girls were sent to scour from the countryside, everything in its proper astrological season according to Culpeper's Herbal. All spring Mary had been pestering folk to take tansy boiled in beer, as a safeguard against damp. Then she fried tansy with eggs to cure the bad stomachs resulting from her medicines. She boiled blackthorn to stop menstrual bleeding and John Lockwood shouted, "Nature'll stop thee bleedin' long before you two have found husbands!" The leaves and flowers were dried and sewn into little paper bags that were hung from the ceiling near to the fireplace in the kitchen, where a large astrological chart was painted on the wall. Roots hung in strings there, also; seeds were stored in nests of oak drawers; and the juices of the stalks were bruised out with a pestle and mortar, the liquids refined by simmering, and stored in glass bottles, a little oil floating on top to preserve them. Mary processed her herbs with an intensity as if she was sure that a spiritual potency lurked within their prophylactic powers. It was only her position as the daughter of a landowner that saved her from being swung as a witch in an iron cage on Beacon Hill in Halifax — in fact, it was to keep her from that fate that John Lockwood schemed to marry her to a clergyman.

But William gave all his attention to Sarah. He rested his eyes upon her with such unwavering authority that she blushed. Then he

12

pressed her hand and found it hot and sticky. Her father's enemies had paid a consumptive weaver who was banished to the moors to spit in the Ewood well and, blaming the rich for his troubles, he had gladly sneaked in during the night and contaminated the Lockwood water. If John Lockwood had not believed that women shouldn't be taught to read and write — skills only for "making out" bills and documents, a man's necessities — Sarah might have pined away her life reading the volumes which, with their freshly-printed smells like bread from the oven, her father's clients would have been glad to bring for her. Instead Sarah spent her life in lonely wandering. From earliest childhood she had grown up with an impulse to flight. At seven years of age she had been thrilled by the thick stone ropes of gargoyles and goblins peering from the Ewood roofs, because it seemed to her that they had escaped from somewhere. Almost as soon as she could walk, she learnt to rush around the Ewood grounds on a pony and soon she was off to the moors. The moors! How differently she felt up there! Climbing them she was breathless with excitement for the moment when she would burst over the rim of the valley and see stretched level before her that boggy space, little mists twining in the hollows, curlews or larks above and distant hills rising like animals waking from slumber. When she grew to be a young woman she would hide in hollows and let the sun caress her, with her gown loosened at her throat and pulled up to her knees. As she felt the sun coming out from behind a cloud she would stretch in ecstasy, oh! oh! here it was! — a beast named July or August, heavy with scents, squatting upon her, she writhing with joy. It burnt her skin and she coughed. If she had entered polite society she would have been shunned as a peasant because of her brown skin: her father told her so, but she didn't care. She loved the moors in the autumn also, when the heather was out and poor people went to pick whinberries. The sunlight swept everything into a golden bowl that washed out all blemishes and was pervaded with nostalgia. She felt that her secret self was liberated up there.

It was through her moorland horse-riding that Sarah kept contact with William Grimshaw and she found out that he had the same ardency as herself for roaming the hills. He seemed to *be* like the moors — strong, dark and brooding. She began to clatter noisily up and down outside his lodgings, which were in a house aptly named "Stones" — it was on a steep hillside above the oak trees, just below a fringe of rocks eroded into soft bulbous forms that were like bales

13

of cloth, and upon which stood a prehistoric stone monument. One day Sarah sought shelter there from a storm and another time William freed her horse entangled in an oak tree. Once she caught him without his wig: his natural hair was black, thick and curly. After a few weeks Sarah definitely loved him; yes, she was certainly in love. It was a paradoxical emotion. She wanted to swamp him with herself and with everything she had, yet she also wished to make herself small enough to become completely absorbed in him. She grew bolder and as she cantered away cackling with laughter, she shouted over her shoulder, "I shall throw my cap at you!" a sickly brilliant glitter in her eye.

William was in need of a good match. His parents came from a branch of their family that had long since been pruned off from the grander Grimshaws. His father had been a rebellious young man who mixed with Ranters and had therefore been "dispossessed" — his cottage burnt, the nearby common enclosed by a lord — so he turned into a wandering labourer, often sleeping in the shelter of gorse bushes on the commons, sometimes going mad at a fair and sometimes for the warmth entering a Dissenters' meeting house. Wrapped in worn-out leather, as he shuffled along the tracks he tried to keep warm inside him the memory of a village in which he had once tended his father's cow and poultry on the common land. Eventually all his rebellious instincts were numbed and then he settled down again in Brindle, thanks to the small dowry of Ann Firth, a servant girl. The couple sacrificed themselves to send both their sons, William and John, to Blackburn School and then on to Christ's College, Cambridge, from whence William came to Todmorden. As he now told Sarah, "The usual reason for takin' Holy Orders is getting a good livin', or bread. I confess it was mine."

Grimshaw fell in love with this wild yet frail creature who came with quick darts and flashes in and out of his life. He longed for her presence and he wasted hours imagining how at their next meeting he would dare to touch her wrist. Yes, Grimshaw had grown timid! He day-dreamed, seeing her form in other women. He let days waste away in an agonised counting of time.

"I shall love thee until I die and ever afterwards," he declared.

"Until death is enough for me and is a long way away, I hope," she answered.

"I mean it."

"When we are married can we travel? To Italy? To Russia?"

"Anywhere! Everywhere!"

Her father was glad to find her choosing a man like himself — of yeoman stock but never misjudging himself in society, apparently suffering no uncertainties — as if Eternity had given them both a fully satisfying explanation of the meaning of life. Yet William suffered a secret and unreasonable melancholy, its only expression being the rapping of his footsteps up and down the floorboards during his sleepless hours. When his courtship with Sarah passed into the stage of long undisturbed conversations, his melancholy temperament helped him to understand her mostly-hidden unhappiness which, she believed, had brought on her consumption. If it was the spit in the well, why wasn't Mary or anyone else amongst the family and servants consumptive? Sarah felt the first thrust of a pain in her chest when her first husband died. Whilst weeping for her second, when for week after week the muscles of her throat stiffened and ached and she almost became dumb, she instinctively knew that it would turn into consumption. Her cheeks felt heated as if with a constant blush or as if she had been sitting too long before a fire. She tried to cool them by splashing them with cold water but that seemed only to make them glow even more. She began to have nose-bleeds. Mary doctored her, without daring to admit that it was consumption, until the point was reached when the servants were all talking about it anyway.

Sarah needed a companion on her rambles, for the Lockwoods were envied and hated by many and her sister was said to be a witch. There were strange travellers on the roads — families driven from their homes by the enclosures, merchants who had not seen their wives for weeks, criminals and footpads. The cottagers seemed inexplicably restless and malevolent, brooding about something. The moorlands of West Yorkshire had been for centuries a hiding place of rebels, and their heirs felt that the prosperous Lockwoods were betraying them. Sarah taught William to behave more compassionately towards the unfortunates whom they met. From her he learnt the pastor's gift of healing. Now that he did not merely lecture them, give them charity or tell them to laugh their troubles away, they felt that they had been visited by a warmer personality. His laughter involved his eyes and ceased to be an embattled expression of his teeth and mouth. In her company he grew tender towards wounded animals and birds. He even got hold of volumes of Latin poets and read them aloud to Sarah.

15

"I love to enter the countryside," he said. "So rich, so peaceful."

"And I like to think of the countryside entering me," she laughed. "As a spirit, as a force — the storm, the lightning from the moors seem to enliven me when it is I who am peaceful."

They used to climb through the woods to Midgley, where women came to their doors, gaped and curtsied to the daughter of Mr Lockwood who was being courted by the curate from Todmorden. Grimshaw showed off his sweetheart by kissing her in the street. (The old women sighed but seemed to love it — then afterwards Sarah would spot them sneering behind her back.) Beyond Midgley they dropped down steeply to Luddenden, passed the church and went up to Luddenden Dean, along the noisy stream, the "loud woodland" meant by the word, the very sound of which — say it slowly, "Lud-den-den" — was like the crashing of water muffled in deep holes amongst rocks and trees. It was a botanist's paradise and Sarah kept pressed flowers in a chap-book. William shot pole-cats and pine-martens, squirrels, the odd fox there. On 20th September 1734 they walked out together late at night to watch the eclipse of the moon.

Sarah would have excited spurts of energy and then need to rest, when a hot flush rose in her cheeks and she almost choked. During one of these pauses she first unpinned her cap and showed William how long, fair and thick her hair was. Another time, after William had mopped up one of Sarah's nose-bleeds, he first touched the top of her breast. They seemed to share one single feeling between them — William, full of love, even flushed like Sarah. The couple sometimes wondered whether they could bear the responsibility of love — of each having to shoulder not only the joy, but also two people's suffering. If Sarah had a toothache, William felt it as acutely as she did. He was pained as she struggled with breathlessness. And yet this burden was part of the happiness, it was the night-time in the lap of which the day rested.

William and Sarah were married on 5th June 1735. "Look upon your husband as one beyond whom there is nothing but Death and Hell. Inquire only into ways of pleasing him," the vicar of Halifax told the bride.

"When are *you* going to marry, Mary?" William asked at the feast.

"Nay, I'll be slave to no man."

"Then thalt be hanged as a witch."

"That's as maybe."

That night Sarah stared at William's naked body: his arm muscles, his square shoulders the breadth of which gave his walk its peculiar roll, the strong legs from continual walking. She lay giggling in bed, the counterpane pulled teasingly up to her chin whilst his eyes that seemed even blacker than usual in the twilight gave her that calm appraising look which she had often seen him cast over a congregation before he began his sermon. Then suddenly he seemed to be everywhere at once — behind her, squeezing her, licking her toes. As he made love to her she imagined that she was on the moors with hill upon hill gently rolling away from under her feet and the air filled with the scent of heather. Dizziness and a feeling of flight, of being sucked into space, became overwhelming and she came into orgasm. She often employed her fantasy of being sucked into space when they made love.

William's younger brother John, who now in his turn was studying at Cambridge, came to the wedding and took a cool look at the Calder Valley as seemingly a good place for a curate to settle in. Their parents also drove over from West Lancashire. Smallholders who counted their pennies, they were nervous about this marriage into the "gentry". William's mother's experience of grand houses was from service in their kitchens and his father knew them through travelling from back door to back door in search of work. The old folks' unease and gratitude at Ewood Court was so embarrassing that John Lockwood intimated that in future they should stay put in Brindle and not come begging at *his* door. The parents, content that their son was so well-matched, obligingly went home to settle into an obscure old age whilst William, in a passing thought, wondered at the dreadful destruction of his father's spunk and rebelliousness. Meanwhile William and his bride moved into the Todmorden parsonage, near to the church and the Hall. It was at the centre of town and the pit of the valley, overhung by the nubs of the hills, the tangles of oak woods and a litter of moss-swamped boulders. At night they heard the streams clattering through the wilderness above them and often, night or day, they heard Todmorden Hall ring with the mad cries of the Quakers.

A thirteen-year-old girl, Molly Shackleton, was found as a maid

17

for Sarah. Molly was a weaver's daughter, one of fourteen children. Pale and small, her mouth stuck open, she was like a bone hung with rags and a little white flesh. She had pored over tedious work in her parents' cottage — putting nails into the leather-backed "cards" that were used for combing out the wool, or with her bare feet trampling it into animal or human urine to cleanse it of grease — ever since she was old enough to control her hands and before she could walk properly. A mole-like defeated slave who never dared straighten her back to indulge herself with daylight or idleness, she walked alone down from her wild home amongst hills, peat bogs, heather and whinberry, clutching a bundle of threadbare dresses, aprons and a bag of herbs, mostly thyme, as a present for her mistress. Going into a consumptive household could have no extra fears for her and she was in awe at serving one of the Lockwoods and at residing in the Parsonage.

William meanwhile was engrossed in his great, secret joy. In their bedroom he sometimes lit fires of coals that.lasted half the night. His happiness made his very bowels quiver. Every organ trembled inside him. When Sarah locked her legs around him as he entered her, his intestines seemed about to melt into a river and flow out of him. His lips snuffled her neck, ear and breasts. Sometimes he kissed her opening, with his soft full lips that were as fleshy as the rose between her legs. Often he was happy just to look at her when she didn't know it. With a fixed smile because he had forgotten himself, he studied the removing of caps, shoes, gowns and silk petticoats — irreplaceable, rich clothes that were the diminishing legacy of Ewood, for William's stipend was only fourteen pounds a year and the Quaker owners of Todmorden Hall refused to pay church dues to an Anglican. She would catch his absorbed attention and turn to him, smiling, for an explanation. The real centre of William's life was not his parish duties, but Sarah, Sarah, Sarah.

John Lockwood was in a hurry to obtain a male heir because of Sarah's consumption. On Mary's advice he sent to Todmorden Parsonage bushels of French beans because they "engendered sperm and incited venery". He need not have worried. Ten months after the marriage Sarah gave birth to a healthy son on 20th April 1736. It rained torrentially, carving gullies down the hillsides, filling cellars and low-lying hovels, and blocking roads with landslides of earth and grit. The whole landscape was changed overnight. The child was delivered at Ewood in a suffocating excess of delight because there was at last a male heir to the Lockwoods. The rush-lights were lit all day. With the flooded cellars below and the glowering sky crackling with lightning above, Mary went around muttering prophecies of disaster. A few days later the child was baptised with John Lockwood's name at Luddenden.

Chapter 2

SARAH HELD WILLIAM as if she personified the wide green country-side; she was the new secret valley where he went hunting; each night he raised her skirts in the same manner that earlier, when he had come in from his day's work, he lifted the lid off a pot on the stove — a hungry bulky unashamed man coming for his rightful meal — and in return next day Sarah encouraged William to take his clerical duties much more seriously, hoping he might become a bishop. He put his gun away and hunted sinners instead of birds and animals. To the larger congregations drawn to his church he loyally read out the speeches of King and Parliament and he had bells rung and bonfires lit for Tory victories. In the churchyard there was a school for a hundred scholars where William taught legal procedures, property rights and mathematics to the blue-gowned sons of prospering clothiers who, having often been cheated, approved of these subjects more than the Greek and Latin taught by Grimshaw's predecessor. Meanwhile the Lockwood trade seemed to fatten on their clerical connection — more cloth, loaded onto long chains of carts, crossed Yorkshire to Hull and thence into Europe, whilst the grass in the Lockwood enclosures grew long and thick on imported bone-fertiliser.

Grimshaw spent his leisure time playing with his baby or reading divine literature: he was trying to placate God because of Sarah's increasing illness which he felt was a punishment for their happiness. He had a large account book, bound in calf leather, in which he credited his good works and balanced them against his sins — his expenditure of his store of God's Grace. Each evening last thing before his prayers, William ruled off the bottom of a page and calcu-lated what credit he still had remaining with God. As carefully as any tradesman he kept a weekly balance and a monthly one — using a bit of tolerance, he managed to keep the balance straight — with a final reckoning at the end of the year. Sarah was comforted to have by their bedside this record of her husband's good works in Todmorden — children baptised, gifts to beggars, employment found for old soldiers, and sinners despatched with a blessing into the everlasting world. Grimshaw approached everyone firmly, nobly and without equivocating. In his parish business he got his own way through patience and subtlety rather than by force. What happiness and security she felt in this man!

A year after John, in March 1737, Sarah gave birth to a sickly daughter who was baptised Jane. The mother had no milk for her baby and Sarah never recovered. Her appetite for the moors weakened and she stayed more and more in bed, her skin fading to the same yellow-grey colour and grainy texture as the millstone-grit gravestones outside the windows. But John Lockwood refused to take her decline seriously. He would not give in to his enemies who had spat consumptive phlegm into his well. He left the door open, slapped his daughter on the back, told her to get up and attend to her children. Blustering to mask his fears he cursed Mary's and all apothecaries' physic and forced Sarah to exercise. With his great palms he raised her upright. He tried to rejuvenate her by talking about the profitability in Amsterdam and Rotterdam of the cloth named after her. But he never dared look Sarah in the face and went out of the room to dab his eyes. William also struggled to remain bluff and cheerful. He deliberately slammed doors heartily and shouted whilst Sarah turned onto him her sad eyes, grown huge in her shrunken face and full of an unintended reproval of his health. Her weakness made her tired of his love and Sarah now felt herself swamped by two powerful men, who were prodigal with their health and still seemed fated to live forever.

William played energetically with his children, particularly adoring their daughter Jenny — the golden halo about her head in the sun, her frail bird-like bones, her first tottering steps through the world in which she like her mother did not seem to expect to stay for long. Delighting Sarah with another characteristic of truly strong men, William handled his children with exquisite gentleness. After their swaddling had been removed, William would hold the children high in his arms and run through the graveyard to excite them with the rush of wind. Sarah watched from the window, happy whilst her husband showed his two tiny infants the small flowers that grew in cracks between the gravestones. When John was three and Jenny two, their father fixed up a game of peg-a-hoop in the nursery. A wooden hoop the size of a dinner plate was suspended from the ceiling and had to be swung so as to land upon a hook fixed to the wall.

The children, too young to succeed themselves, had faces shining with joy at their father's skill. As soon as William came home, no matter how tired he was, his face broke into a smile that creased the corners of his eyes whilst the children dragged him off to their nursery, meanwhile drawing out of him the fantastic stories which he had been steadily embroidering for them during the day, to occupy his mind whilst he was obliged to pretend to listen to over-much village piety.

"Tell us what happened today, Papa! Tell us what happened!"

> "Why, I met an old man
> Who wouldn't say his prayers,
> So I took him by the left leg
> And threw him down the s-t-a-i-r-s!"

Grimshaw shouted, swinging the infants around him as if to throw them, also, about the house.

"You told us that before!" John laughed, in the teasing manner which he had inherited from his father. William always felt most ashamed to come home without something new for his children. One day he brought a roll of mysterious mouldy parchments, the astrological predictions of his predecessor the Reverend Henry Krabtree who wrote, even in the parish register, that the Roman Empire would because of Christ last a further two thousand years, when would follow the universal kingdom of the Jews, before the final destruction of the world and the Second Coming.

"A black boy from Africa's been found in Todmorden. Now you haven't heard *that* before!" William said one day.

"It were a collier coming from t' pit," John responded, flatly.

"That it weren't, it were a nigger boy I tell you, black as a chimney! He escaped from his master's coach in Burnley and walked all over the hills to get here. His clothes were torn and his face bleeding because the dogs and the boys of the town chased him, wanting to kill him and steal the silver collar off his neck, until at last he sought refuge with me."

"Why 'aven't you brought him home for us, Papa?" Jane asked.

"Because the name of his owner was engraved on his collar and it was honest to return him."

"He'll be flogged for running away," John said dreamily, fascinated. "Worse than the boys in the school. Skin'll be flayed off him. I'm going t'Africa when I grow up, to cetch me own niggers."

22

(The children didn't really believe their father's story, any more than his other fantastic tales, until a few days later when they overheard Molly complaining to their mother, "They say black men and foreigners is taking over Todmorden.")

Meanwhile the children enjoyed hours of games with their father. He dressed up in strange clothes and acted the parts of the Devil, of God visiting the Garden of Eden (for which the infants played Adam and Eve) and various scenes with the Old Testament prophets. He carried his children on his back, threw them in the air, even irreverently pushed them in a wheelbarrow around the graveyard, whilst reciting Isaac Watts' *Divine Songs For Children*.

> "Whene'er I take my walks abroad
> How many poor I see!
> What shall I render to my God
> For all his gifts to me?"

"I don't like that, it's lackin' cheerfulness," John said.

"Neither do I!" Grimshaw answered, and went back to traditional rhymes:

> "Little lad, little lad,
> Where wast thou born?
> Far off in Lancashire
> Under a thorn,
> Where they sup sour milk
> From a ram's horn!"

Then the fun was stopped by the sound of their mother's awesome coughing from another room. William, believing that his wife was about to be snatched into the Everlasting Kingdom, dashed from his children, who however were not prevented from stealing to the door to witness the climax of their mother's coughing.

His wife's first haemorrhage stunned William and after it he became strikingly quieter, considerate of her need to shelter within herself and give out nothing to anyone. Partly so that William could enjoy a rest, Sarah was moved out of their bedroom and had a permanent invalid's couch set up downstairs by the window through which she could watch the snowdrops, heather and yellow hawkbit as they flowered in season between the crammed stones of the graveyard and drifting across the hills. Her couch became the anchorage of Sarah's life; she had all the room's furniture re-arranged so that it

23

could catch the sun and around it the clutter of a sickbed. There was a present of handkerchiefs from Ewood, and she kept near her the portfolio of pressed flowers collected during her courtship. Sometimes her father brought her oranges and various medicines brewed by Mary, who visited in clothes smelling of wormwood and camomile.

"I have been forsaken by God," Grimshaw said — sounding guilty about this as he spoke to Molly, and almost with envy for her plumpness at the Parsonage whilst her mistress sickened. "After each winter we grow hopeful of her survival but always she worsens later. She trembles like a sick chicken and hardly has the strength to clear her lips of the blood. Her forehead is as if covered with dew, her days have no happiness but for watching the flowers that she loves outside the window. And my own weariness has now made me nearly blind to her sufferings."

"They say that she can be cured with the odours of a cowshed," Molly said hopefully. They tried taking Sarah out to one, but as her couch was turned she thought she was being placed in the right position for being carried out feet-first for her burial and her eyes flared like a terrified horse's. Next they brought buckets of manure to her bedside, but she fainted from the treatment.

William lost weight and grew dull and listless. He could not remember quite simple things, a twitch developed in his cheek and he was irritable. He who normally was so sure of himself began to stammer and could not make decisions. "Molly!" he stammered. "I cannot swallow. There is a lump like an egg in my throat." Yet he still would not allow his brother John (who had followed William's example and had come as a curate to nearby Cross Stone) to replace him at Sarah's bedside: he felt that only he himself could prepare her to meet her Maker.

The couple did not look at each other very often. One day, when the two small children were brought for their daily visit to their mother, Sarah struggled to recite a rhyme to them:

> "Rock-a-bye baby,
> Thy cradle is green,
> Father's a nobleman,
> Mother's a queen,
> And Jenny's a lady,
> And wears a golden ring,
> And Johnny's a drummer,

24

And drums for the king. . . ."

But she hadn't the strength to finish it. Husband and wife then tried
the fearful experiment of searching each other's faces and it was
unbearable. The grief broke out and it was no good for either of
them to repeat an exchange of glances.

Sarah suffered half a dozen haemorrhages at the end of her life.
No-one present ever forgot the smell in her room — twenty years
later Molly Shackleton had only to get a whiff of a cowshed or a
butcher's yard, to remember her mistress's end. When it seemed that
each day would be Sarah Grimshaw's last, Molly was breathless with
rushing to Ewood and Cross Stone to bring the family together.
During what looked like being Sarah's last hour, when her father,
her sister Mary, her children, Molly Shackleton and John Grimshaw
were present, grovelling and praying, William brought to Sarah's
bedside the cup of wine and the cross for final Communion. The
queer thought passed through his mind that her last breaths sounded
like an orgasm. At sight of what he had brought, the shred of her
lung let out an amazing terrible shriek. It was as if she was trying to
empty it as quickly as possible rather than to protest at leaving life.
William, trembling, the muscles twitching in his cheek, pushed the
wine and the bread onto her lips, whereupon Sarah began a grue-
some begging and to kick violently with her legs, her lips reddened by
a spill of wine just managing to hold the wafer. It was perhaps this
effort which did finally extinguish her. She fell still and William even
before testing her breath sensed that Sarah's soul had left her body.
What was left was like the mere wax image of a woman. It was suddenly hard to believe that the corpse left behind had ever been Sarah.
It seemed as if God had removed her and left a substitute.

After Sarah's death William was almost paralysed, except that to the
twitch in his face was added a rapid writhing movement of his
shoulders. Otherwise he moved very slowly. Though weary, he was
unable to sleep, conditioned to a state of irritable fatigue. The lump
came in his throat whenever he tried to eat although Molly nursed
him with the softest, milkiest food. He had been twenty-five when he
met Sarah and he was thirty-one when she died, but he looked as
though not six but ten years had passed — his face was sallow and
his hair grey so that he now rarely removed his wig. He was the
reverse of his previous self. He was tense and unfriendly, as if he felt

threatened. He had grown thin. The preacher who had been famous for his rhetoric became preoccupied and almost dumb, or he stammered. He sat for hours fixed to his chair, giving out a soft asthmatic wheezing, then suddenly he would explode into a rapid fire of angry words, his cheeks would flush and he would sweat. This anger focussed on Molly. He was normally the most self-controlled of men, but now the slightest thing could upset him — a door closed, or one left open. Thank goodness the girl had grown capable in the time she had been with the Grimshaws! After his outbursts he would subside into nervousness, when he blubbered like a child through his soft rubbery lips. He mumbled that nothing interested him any more; he had ceased to feel either sorrow or joy.

Molly and Mary Lockwood washed Sarah's body, dressed her, changed the bed linen and fumigated the room with brimstone. William did not seem to understand what they were doing. "What's that?" he said, his eyes glistening, frightened as this noise startled his reveries. "Is that Sarah?" They treated him as a madman. Once as William sat paralysed except for his twitches, he muttered "There . . . is . . . no . . . God!" Another time he grasped John with a hug like a whirlpool, as if he was trying to suck his brother into his own desolation. "At night I lust after her body still," he confessed. The children were taken out of his way to Ewood, for fear they might discover their father with their mother's corpse, and everyone wondered whether William would be fit to attend Sarah's funeral.

John Grimshaw made the arrangements. Without fuss he sent out invitations, ordered half an ox for roasting, five gallons of port and claret, cakes to be baked and a sermon from Dr Legh, the vicar of Halifax. He stood balefully at the Parsonage door and handed out pairs of black gloves to the mourners as they arrived. William's parents took their pieces of funeral cake and glasses of wine and entered with the things they had prepared for saying during the long journey from Brindle now stillborn on their lips, hearing Molly Shackleton sobbing in the dark passageway and wondering whereabouts within their son must be hidden.

William bravely followed Sarah's coffin, which was slung on a litter between two horses and taken six miles to Luddenden. The autumn leaves sifted through the grey air and smacked wetly on the coffin as it made its way along the busy packhorse routes, amongst horses laden with wool, with rolls of cloth, with coal brought down from the hills, or with salt on its way from Cheshire. Around the church and in the nearby valley where William had courted Sarah, the trees were hacked down to stumps bleeding with yellow sap, for they had been felled to build ships for the war against Spain. At the funeral service, William felt depressed that Dr Legh obviously knew little about Sarah's character — her impulsive vivacity and the joy she could bring, conjuring it out of nowhere! Her tombstone was no real reminder of her either — composed by John in William's default, it read simply, "Sarah, daughter of John Lockwood of Ewood, Gent., the wife of the Revd. Wm. Grimshaw, Minister of Todmorden, who died Nov. 1. 1739". Afterwards, during the funeral feast at Ewood, William was silent, embarrassed by people whispering and staring aghast at his transformed wasted features, his leaden movements, the twitches that he struggled to control and his air of being pitched into a massive grief. When the early dusk fell and the candles glittered on the wine and on the knives embedded in the great hunks of meat, and when the anecdotes grew drunken and repetitive, William returned home, alone but for Molly Shackleton. The groups of people who had gathered along the route to watch the procession had all gone away and the gig travelled through an empty, damp, starless November night.

Molly, also with grief bottled up inside her, silently lit the rush-lights in the Parsonage then crept away to tidy the rooms deserted by the funeral party and to restore the fires, as if to drive away the chill of death. William was virtually alone, Molly was so quiet. It seemed somewhere other than his own home. He existed in an aching vacuum. He missed the bawling of his infants, the coughing of his wife and the wailing of mourners. Molly coped with grief by making herself busy, but he had nothing to do and the empty Parsonage terrified him. He could not bear the blank look of the walls. The graveyard outside was silent and empty because townsmen out of respect for their parson no longer made short cuts through it from the inn. He took a light into his study, pointlessly picking things up and setting them down again. Molly slid discreetly into the kitchen that he had vacated and he heard her banking up the fire. Like a thief, he listened for her sounds. The fire crackled. Dishes clattered. He could not sit where the shadows flickered like human forms, like Sarah's form. Nor could he move, go into the room where the deserted sickbed was, enter the bedroom where his wife's clothes were stored in a chest.

Grimshaw suddenly gave in to the spasms that jerked his cheeks. They spread to his jaw and finally the whole upper part of his body was writhing whilst his legs felt cold and paralysed. "There is no God! The Universe is no more than a machine, like a mill or a clock, wheels turning within wheels!" This echoing thought seemed the only live thing in his skull, flitting there like a bat in a cave. He knelt on the floor, facing the window through which came a murky evening light fading quickly into night. "God save me from this doubt!" he prayed and there was a fine sweat upon his brow, like the one on Sarah every night.

Molly came to say "good night," but she saw his hands and shoulders shaking, his fever, his intense devotions, and she left without a word, to whisper her prayers in private. When William climbed into bed he actually slept, but he woke in an hour or so without reason. His sleep must have been very deep and he did not know how long it had been. A moon had risen, glazing his room with foggy light. He felt an utter loneliness and a tightness across his chest. He turned to his pillow and wept.

The next day seemed to refresh him for a few moments. He forced himself to rise and begin the day by pacing between walls that he wanted to beat with his fists for their indifference to restoring his Sarah to him. He could not face this impossibility. Instead he imagined that she was alive again. He heard her voice and particular laughter — it used to begin with wild energy and then collapsed for lack of breath. Molly prepared an oatmeal porridge but his throat felt constricted and he could not eat. He tried to form words to speak but he could not do that either. William felt a new symptom: his heart seemed swollen, so that it filled the whole of his chest, a great pumping organ like a village well. In his study he prayed once again. He was terrified of being cursed by God for his doubts. Since Sarah's death, he had become steadily more certain that God was a cruel implacable being who would give no mercy.

Eventually Grimshaw turned to work for salvation and tackled it ferociously. He tired himself out, walking the hills both day and night. Once he almost went over the edge of a cliff in the dark and when he pulled back from it he felt sorry that either God or the Devil had not taken him at that moment. And yet when he reached the moorland cottages to which he had been called, he could often hardly communicate with his parishioners. He saw, at this time, a new improvement to the looms — almost the first one for a thousand

28

years. A local man, William Kay, had invented his "flying shuttle": a gadget of strings and bits of wood with which the weaver without pausing in his work could operate a hammer to fire the shuttle. Thus the journeyman or apprentice, who had often stood at the side of the loom to send the shuttle across, was done away with. Also the new loom worked faster, but the spinners — the women of the neighbourhood — could not spin more wool, so competition increased amongst the weavers and families starved. One poor moor-edger who could not face the winter cut his throat, but he made a bloody mess of it and died horribly, slowly, in his barn amongst his blackened oats. The parson, called to bring the peace of God to his family, could only remark grimly, "I don't know how soon I must do the same." And when he saw a searching look in the eyes of his flock as they came to console him for his own bereavement, Grimshaw turned away abruptly, unable to bear that either. He who had been so purposeful was now weak and without determination. Sometimes after struggling by peat holes, cliffs and boulders he would see the cottage where people waited for him, and he would hesitate, shaking with nerves, and return to the Parsonage unable to understand his own irresolution and cowardice.

One Sunday he collapsed on his pulpit steps. The congregation saw his podgy hand grasp the stair rail, as he hovered for a moment and fell heavily. They carried him into the churchyard and laid him flat upon a tombstone. As he recovered beneath a circle of faces swimming back to him through the wintry air he felt that he had a vision, seeing them all clearly for the first time. Their features were marked by the fear of poverty if God ruined their crops or if storms or French pirates took the clothiers' ships in the channel; by incurable deformations from illness. Staring vertiginously upwards into a ring of faces, Grimshaw felt that he was looking down into the bottomless pit of Hell, where people who had committed only the same offences as himself were staring up at him, terrified, condemned. He saw, mirrored in their faces, his own unpunished sins being shaken at him like lighted torches. Whereupon he got up, marched determinedly back to his pulpit and with something of the old Grimshaw returned to him, thundered at his congregation that smelled of wet kersey-cloth and of animal manure: "My friends, we are all in a damnable state and I scarcely know how we are to get out of it!" — words that echoed around Todmorden for months afterwards.

But his greatest problem was lust. He lusted after Molly who from imitating her mistress often looked like Sarah when she leaned in a doorway, and he quickly spun his eyes from the sight. One Sunday during Communion the Devil roused him with a woman who knelt before him at the altar rail, and there was an involuntary stirring of flesh beneath his gown as he placed the Communion biscuit on her lips. Eventually the account book that he had begun during Sarah's illness became so full of sins that, as he tumbled into debt, he like any other bankrupt ceased to keep any accounts at all.

A picture of the Virgin Mary was found among Krabtree's remains. Grimshaw kept it and he reached the nadir of grief and hopelessness when, one evening whilst struggling to pray, he imagined her glittering blue silk dress rustling to her knees and her body stepping out of it and coming towards his bed. He stopped his prayers and touched that part of his body which it was a sin to touch. Afterwards, spent and tired, he detested himself, desperate for a means of killing the dragon that once more confronted a Grimshaw.

The melancholia that purged Grimshaw was at that time fashionable throughout Todmorden, wrapping itself like a black scarf around the place. Funeral cards decorated with scrolls and ghoulish emblems of mortality, skulls and crossbones and plundered treasure chests, were passed around the town. These same symbols were carved on tombstones. One woman, following a suggestion brought to her by a salt pedlar from Cheshire, went so far as to have a punch-bowl like the most delicate and transparent china made out of the skull of her dead child. William's brother John Grimshaw was now courting Mary Cockcroft, a fashionably melancholic lady who was constantly reminding him to be unhappy. She would only go out with him if he would take her amongst graves and ruins. John submitted though he was bored and baffled, hiding his yawns whilst Mary searched for owls and bats amongst ivy-clad masonry. This couple and other friends used to console William with volumes of the new literature of melancholy, and he learnt from these books to spend part of every day contemplating his own funeral in the grave-yard that surrounded his house or by Sarah's grave at Luddenden. He was always looking for an excuse to walk in that direction. Once he contemplated the vision of their wedding rings loose about their bones, and he began a poem on this subject, but was disturbed by woodcutters. Afraid of being shut in a madhouse he forgot his verses and strode into the village, rubbing his limbs that had become locked with cold.

In another moment of passion he wrote down preparations for his own funeral. "Whenever Almighty God is pleased to receive my soul, I require my executors to bury my body in the same grave with my deceased wife Sarah at Luddenden. To attend my funeral I wish 20 persons to be invited and entertained in the following manner. Let 5 quarts of claret be put into a punch-bowl. Let everyone have a penny roll of bread to eat therewith and let all sit down together as an emblem of Christian love — this at home. At the drinking house let everyone have a quart of ale, a two-penny sliced cake and afterwards a glass of claret." There then followed an account to the amount of £5, including "To a funeral sermon . . . 10/6. To church dues . . . 5s. To 2 gallons of claret . . . 13/4. To 25 pairs of gloves . . . £1." Meanwhile, his dizziness, his twitching, the lump that rose in his throat, palpitations, the irresolution that would unaccountably overpower him and the feeling of something huge in his stomach, still continued. People expected Grimshaw eventually to be locked in the madhouse, whilst he himself waited for the Devil to call him. There was no hope.

One day as Grimshaw opened yet another new volume, he felt a great light flash from its pages. He blinked, wondering whether a nearby row of pewter plates had caused it. But when he closed the book, the light disappeared — only to appear again when he opened the title page. It was so blinding and hot that his cheeks flushed. His lips blubbered as if he was about to fall into a fit. This was like the miracle that appeared to St Paul on the road to Damascus! He had received a signal from God telling him that at last he would find his salvation in this book! It was Dr Owen's *Doctrine of Justification by Faith*. William studied it throughout one long day. Its message was that he must accept total, abject dependence upon God's power. He prayed through the following night for this. At first as he prayed, he was conscious of other sounds — the whisperings of the landscape or the inhalations and exhalations of the house as if he was inside a great lung of wood and stone. So long as he heard these things, he knew that he was not concentrating sufficiently. To aid him he ritualistically repeated the Lord's Prayer again and again until hypnotised he could hear nothing else but "Our Father which art in Heaven" inside his skull. Eventually he felt a kind of weightlessness, and as his prayer seemed to be answered, a sensation as if his soul was being sweetened.

The next morning, Molly was the first to notice an amazing radiance on William's face, fixed and glossy. Through the catalyst of grief his true character emerged. But to people who had not witnessed his soul's journey, it appeared that his nature had been suddenly, totally reversed. His twitches and irresolution vanished. He became a tyrannical Sabbatarian. Through hunting his erring flock over the moors he also wore out his erotic desires. Instead of seeking joy in nature as in the days with Sarah, he confronted her, defying her at her most malevolent in order to reach his object — the notoriously sinful colliers squatting like black rabbits around the mouths of their burrows driven into the hilltops, and the gangs who were felling and burning the last of the forests or building enclosure walls. He burst arrogantly into stone shacks (wealthy parishioners were not so easily brow-beaten) to accuse frightened weavers of sliding down the slippery slopes to Hell. Why did they scuffle out of his way because they had not been to church, but when they were struck by misfortune come to him in helpless distress as their last appeal before God and Eternity? After he had "reproved" them that benign gloss returned to his face. There was no arguing with that.

William began to pray four times a day — coming to kneel before God with the slumbrous peace of an ox brought down by the ring in its nose to kneel before the slaughter-man's axe. He took up the account book of his sins once more and set the balance right by fasting and extra prayers, but he nevertheless began to grow sleek and fat again. He read Thomas Brooks' *Precious Remedies Against Satan's Devices*, discovered that the Devil had thirty-six ways to tempt one into sin and, like a hypochondriac who has stumbled on a medical book, felt sure that he was the victim of each of them. William wrote out a private contract with God, modelled upon one in Philip Doddridge's *Rise and Progress of Religion in the Soul,* its masturbatory language as repetitive and insistent as pornography:

Eternal and unchangeable Jehovah! I desire with the deepest humiliation and abasement of soul to fall down in Thine awful presence, and earnestly pray that Thou wilt penetrate my heart with a sense of Thine unutterable and inconceivable glories! Trembling may justly take hold upon me when I a sinful worm presume to lift up my head to thee, presume to appear in Thy majestic presence on such an occasion as this!

32

And so on for a great many pages. Afterwards, as Doddridge instructed, William shut himself away, fasting on his knees for a day. In the evening he read the document aloud, signed it and locked it away like a dirty secret.

Now his sermons scourged his Todmorden flock, telling them only to have faith and to come to the Lord in total submission, when they would receive the sublime knowledge that their sins had been forgiven and that they had received the promise of a Heavenly Kingdom. This staggered them because previously they had been told that they would not know their eternal reward until the moment of death. With their memories of jovial Grimshaw, the fishing and card-playing parson, they resented the burly black figure of "Mad Grimshaw" (as they now began to call him) who came up their farm tracks with an unmistakable purposefulness like a bull gathering momentum for a charge, to tell them to renounce their sinful joys of singing, dancing, playing the fiddle; and instead to pray, fast and deny themselves.

William decided that he needed another wife to help him avoid the temptation of lust and also as a housekeeper and a mother for his children. He took the nearest available woman: Elizabeth Cockcroft, the sister of Mary Cockcroft who was now John Grimshaw's wife. Then, because his Todmorden parishioners could not accept this new Mad Grimshaw, he sought a move and found himself nominated by the trustees of the church in Haworth. "And where is Haworth?" William Grimshaw asked. "A barbaric mountainous place, bleak and dirty. The barren face of that country is a fit emblem of the inhabitants who have no more religion than their cattle," John Lockwood told him. Its advantage was that it was only a dozen miles from Luddenden and so within easy reach of Sarah's grave.

Chapter 3

IN THE SPRING of 1742, the Grimshaw family in the Lockwood coach toiled over the moors to Haworth, a cart with their belongings rumbling behind. The two children — John was aged six and Jane was five — had grown up in the Calder Valley with a feeling of being confined in a narrow passageway. Now that they were lifted over the jagged cliffs of millstone grit they felt loosed like birds to skim over the sleek moors, grey, blue and violet. The heather was being burnt so as to clear the way for new shoots which would be fertilised with the ash. Clouds of smoke rolled over the landscape above which larks sang at screaming pitch.

"All their nests'll get burned. Thousands and thousands of them, won't they, Papa? All t' nestlings'll be burned alive," John said, his nose pressed to the window. Jane stared wide-eyed at her brother, thinking that he must be teasing because something so horrible could not possibly be true. "T'appens every year," John said, gloating.

They climbed over Scraping Hill where sometimes the smoke cleared and a cluster of dark stones or a frothy waterfall cut the skyline. Then they sank downwards into Haworth parish and once more they were amongst green enclosures filled with cloth. People came out to look at them and every cottage had folk on its doorstep. Some of them even waved "palm" branches — sprays of pussy-willow. John and Jane were nervous and sick because of the jolting of the coach, so they were given some of Aunt Mary's treacle. After that they bucked up or pretended to do so, and began to feel proud before the eyes of their father's new parishioners.

Haworth was huddled on the bleak outcrop of a hill before it dropped suddenly into Keighley. The buildings were a close-packed compromise with the slopes, jutting out at all angles and most of them "back to earth," their lowest storeys burrowing into the hillside. The coach entered at the foot of a tunnel of stone. Bowed walls, stairs rising awkwardly to fit in with the street, lintels, roofs, window frames and even fences were made of stone — it was surprising that

34

the houses were not closed with stone doors, like tombs. Haworth was a tawny-yellow colour like the moorland grass but darkening with the soot from the fires that heated the woolcombers' pots. It was almost entirely a community of hand-loom weavers, spinners, wool-brokers, woolsorters and of the woolcombers whose work-shops, now that the worsted trade was growing, were increasing along the streets. For the sake of the woolcombing process, the workshop windows had to be kept closed, even though the charcoal stoves that heated up the combs gave off poisonous fumes. Water ran everywhere — over walls, down them, under them; off the roofs, across the glistening fields, down the street, from under the doors. There was an air of sickness. Heaps of manure were left in alleyways because they contained chemical ash from the wool processing and farmers did not want to take them for their fields. Manure heaps overflowed into a channel down the centre of the street. Coal smoke caught at the throat.

On this spring day the winter filth was being swilled away. Rushes that had become trampled into solid masses were being dug out of the houses. The manure heaps, the hot rushes and the freshly bared stone floors steamed in the sunlight. At Head Well, children who had been greased with lamb or goose fat and stitched into clothes throughout the winter, were being unstitched, scraped clean and washed down. The arrival of the Lockwood coach was announced up the street by women knocking on the backs of their fireplaces. Pale women and children rose out of basement kitchens and blinked at the light. The woolcombers, who had a reputation for being shrewd, came out of their shops, shivered in the dank air and stared hard at Mad Grimshaw and his family. How would he compare with the last parson? (Isaac Smith had been sacked for wearing casual dress like a workman on Sundays, preaching to dissenters and marrying those who had coupled on impulse after a fair.) A wary silence crept up Main Street a few paces ahead of the Grimshaw party. A loom ceased to bang in an upstairs room. A woman stopped scolding her child. Someone moved a cart out of the way. From one house came the rhythmic banging of the lazy, graceful game of peg-a-hoop. The children brightened at that familiar sound and looked at their father, who was scowling. The game suddenly stopped. But at a few places along the steep slow climb through the echoing stones, a few groups of drunken people totally ignored the arrival of the Grimshaws. They came out of their doors and peed, while from

35

indoors came the noises of arguments and of wild music played on fiddles, which had been going on for most of the previous night.

Elizabeth and the children studied William because their own happiness would depend upon his response to the wild licentiousness that ameliorated village life. He tutted and sucked his teeth but did not speak, whilst inwardly contemplating the opportunity here to establish the Kingdom of God. Elizabeth looked out and noticed the ugly marks of inbreeding on the pale people. Like her predecessor as Grimshaw's wife, she had come from one of the finer houses in the Calder Valley: from Mayroyd near Hebden Bridge. But she was of a different temperament to Sarah. She was more demanding and ambitious, shall we say. She felt that this place was going to attack her with loneliness, misery and neglect. In a strange coach that rang on the stones in the uncanny quiet ahead of her luggage cart and with tense excited children who were not her own, she was suddenly preyed upon by the certainty that she herself would never bear children, but that she would die here. At the top of Main Street she glimpsed the church that was falling into ruins through the Reverend Isaac Smith's neglect, with its stone tiles missing and the savage children clinging to bushes that grew above the windows or out of the eaves, and huddled into the coach to retreat from this dreadful Haworth.

The family's new home was Sowdens, a farmhouse-parsonage half a mile from the town. The party had come in a loop descending onto the building from the moors, near to some quarries. The slopes were bright with newly-opened dandelions and there were primroses at the roadside. Elizabeth was so glad to be able to see over distances again — so far as was possible with the moors on fire, with hamlets and fields of tenters obliterated in smoke. The house was a long low building, the simplest of stone boxes, with one end rammed into the slope of the moor and the other end rising out of it, like a boat cresting a wave. It had one extraordinary feature. At the risen end there was a massive stone porch, so that it looked as though the house had been built onto that rather than the other way round. The porch had great carved corbels like huge knees below its eaves, and beneath its stone-flagged roof was an iron-studded door. It was as if it had been built ready for the entrances and exits of an extraordinarily powerful character — as if in the knowledge that, one day, a Parson Grimshaw would inhabit it.

The Lockwood coach was too grand for the narrow track and it

36

sank its wheels into the drains at the side. Ungainly as it was, the vehicle still looked fabulous to the staring cottagers, the quarrymen and the people waiting at Sowdens. The Grimshaws descended, grandly, condescendingly, into the yard especially swept clean of cattle and poultry droppings. But there was suddenly such a great to-do, with the luggage cart clattering behind them, that all their grandeur collapsed and Elizabeth grew frantic to keep her little family together. John immediately ran off through the cow muck, wanting to explore every corner of his new home at the same moment — dirtying his new shoes and pantaloons, staring at the neighbours' cattle and searching for herbs everywhere in the way that his Aunt Mary had taught him. Jane, still feeling sick, clung to her stepmother and stared. To both of them this place set in bleak moorland seemed a poor and mean home.

Molly Shackleton, who had gone two days ahead of the party, stood at the door. In the seven years she had been with the Grimshaws, she had steadily put on weight and confidence, and now more than Elizabeth looked like the mistress of Sowdens. With her was Jonathan Whitehead, the parish clerk — a nervous weasel of a man holding the parish register ready in his hand — and one of the churchwardens, Thomas Pighells, a man bulky enough to fill out the whole archway. As Pighells stepped forward, he seemed to little Jane like a vast wallowing beast. He spat onto the shining doorstep — he enjoyed spitting and scratching himself — and said bluntly, "Does hee like bull baitin', Parson? And Methodist baitin'? Does t' approve of cock fightin'?"

He was laughing openly at them and a shudder made Elizabeth clutch her arms tightly about her. All the church trustees were powerful clothiers who, like Elizabeth's own family and the Lockwoods in the Calder Valley, ruled the parish by controlling the supply of wool and the sale of cloth. Whilst the parson guarded the gates of Eternity, they had had control of church tithes and dues — and thereby of the parson. Because the Reverend Isaac Smith had been more a friend of the weavers than of themselves they had got rid of him by accusing him in an ecclesiastical court of "wearing unseemly apparel", of being absent from his parish to preach elsewhere and even of something very like witchcraft — of having when he first moved to Sowdens "dedicated it with prayers, aspersions, acclamations and crossings." After Smith, the clothiers and their wives hoped for a tighter control over the woolcombers

37

with the appointment of Grimshaw.

Elizabeth coldly ordered Molly to go and find John and with a tight feeling at her throat she took Jane into the black mouth of the house. A door was open to a living room on the left. It faced south and smoky sunlight poured through a row of windows, its brightness intensifying the shadows. The trustees had furnished the house and there was a vast six-legged oak table, eight feet long, laid with joints of meat and other dishes. The smells of more food came through the kitchen. There was a huge fireplace eight feet wide, drawers and cupboards next to it, high-backed upholstered chairs — a grand one with arms for William, and several without arms so that the ladies could spread their dresses — and a settle beside the fire.

The trustees, standing in the room, watched William Grimshaw as a family of cats watch the hole of a mouse. Glasses were poured with wine, and a thin man in a dandified waistcoat, who looked to Elizabeth like a member of a theatrical company, swiftly struck up a tune on a fiddle. This was Jonas Appleyard, the apothecary. He had made his own sister, Ruth, pregnant and had been married to her by Isaac Smith. What Jonas loved most of all, however, was his fiddle. He took it almost everywhere with him, ever ready to caress from it a wild music that no-one had ever written down but which seemed a natural expression of the moor: a tense nervous sound like the wind through the grass, or like the bleat of frightened sheep or calves. The jig burst out of the fiddle as if it was on fire. "Yorkshire Lasses", it was called. Nobody had any idea where such music originated, but they did not really believe that it had a human origin. Whilst it seemed raw and offensive to "refined taste", the moorland people revered it, listening in ecstasy.

William instantly put up his hand to stop the music. A silence fell on the whole watchful company. The trustees now found out what kind of parson this Grimshaw was and Jonas put his fiddle behind his back, like a child hiding his fingers after stealing jam.

"Do you know 'Oh dear what can the matter be'?" Elizabeth said, to close the silence. "It's a new tune from down London." She hummed the air. It sounded a miserably thin melody to the fiddler, but out of respect he listened carefully, his hand cupped behind his ear. Then he tried to play it, but it came out enriched with the spirit of the moors, full of his own variations.

"No, no, no!" Elizabeth stamped her foot. "It's a *polite* melody, don't waggle your bow about!"

38

Appleyard held his bow stiffly, suddenly made nervous of his instrument. William scowled, for he did not like this frivolous tune any more than the previous one. Elizabeth tried to sing to the fiddle. "Can't you take control of that heathen thing?" she shouted, exasperated. "Can't you do anything in Haworth that's not *brutish?*"

Humbler people visited Sowdens during the following days. Though it was spring and everyone was busy, most found the time to stroll across and test Grimshaw before they heard him in the pulpit. Sometimes there were queues of farmers bringing the smell of the moorland fire into the Sowdens kitchen. Often they found the parson drinking tea, for he had become addicted to it. The visitors came to him not with spiritual but with legal problems . . . they had watched Grimshaw line the tiny six-foot-square "study" above the porch with volumes and take his wig off to sit reading them, and Molly had told them that they were law books. The parishioners had difficulties with the wills of those whom the winter had killed; problems concerning boundaries, water rights and rights upon common lands. The farmers fidgeted nervously before Elizabeth, who was grand and aloof and to make an impression was always dressed in silks. Yet they planted their feet confidently on the ringing stone floor because the place was, after all, still only a farmhouse. Elizabeth felt that William slipped too easily into vulgar expressions in the company of these people. She never thought he would become so much at home in a farmyard, surrounded by the somnambulant rhythms of cattle and the smell of manure. He was now over thirty years old, so Elizabeth despaired of his ever losing the taint of his Lancashire dialect or the manner of a man used to bawling at cattle.

After he had advised his visitors William told them to look for an even happier outcome in the Kingdom of God. They assured him that they already spent more time praying than they did working and that this was why they were in difficulties. How many chances to mend a wall (through which their cow had escaped to trample their neighbours' oats and knock the cloth off his tenters) had been lost because they were at prayer at the time! William, not believing a word of it, rarely gave an absolute judgement, thus making sure that they would return to him for further "exhortations". Grimshaw's new neighbours marked how earnestly he prayed, how unconcernedly he set off through the mud of farmyards and they decided that he would "do". But most of them changed their minds when he turned his attention to the church. Firstly he had all the tiles repaired, the grass and the bushes removed from the gutters and the cracks in the stonework, and he stopped the children from playing there. No-one objected to this. But then, ignoring the traditional date for cleaning out the old rushes, which was in the autumn, he had all the filthy stuff dug out of the nave, the building swept clean and treated with brimstone by Jonas Appleyard.

This appalling defiance of a traditional ceremony was but a beginning. "God's church is not a place in which to play games!" he bawled, and all "crude theatricals" were forbidden. He had a brass altar rail built. The villagers were used to taking Communion around the altar itself, putting their hands upon it "like savages", as Grimshaw said. Now they felt that their religion was being imprisoned and chained down, so they threatened to leap the altar rail during the first service. Within a few weeks Haworth church became as severe as a courtroom, scrubbed and bare, with the last vestiges of older decorations and rituals finally scoured away. William had even eradicated some obscure curved lines, shaped like the crescent moon, which were at the base of the tower — symbols of witchcraft carved by medieval people, Grimshaw said. But these symbols appeared again mysteriously overnight as often as Grimshaw had them removed. The parson also had the old font, which was decorated with griffins and dragons, broken up and a new plain one erected with carved around the brim, "I indeed have bapt'd you with water but He shall baptise you with THE HOLY GHOST." Finally he had a vast three-decker pulpit made. Everyone knew about the days and nights of labour in the carpenter's shop to produce this threat of the powerful speeches with which Grimshaw intended to net congregations who had hardly heard a sermon in their lives before, and were more used to playing in church at "games and rituals".

Nearly a month after he first arrived in Haworth, Grimshaw went to York to sign his acceptance of the Thirty-Nine Articles of the Church of England. (Prowling through York Minster, he thought that the wilderness of columns and tracery was more like a forest for druids than the church of God.) Then he took his first Sunday service. He rose at four o'clock, before the lamps of the farmers were tossed across the darkness between bedroom, kitchen or barn, and he went to meditate in his study above the porch. After an hour of what he called "the soul's chewing", he emerged. The heather fires here and there spurted into life on the moors, and with a similar light dawn was tinting the horizon. A small bird ruffled its feathers in the yard and the first curlew began to call. William felt that powerful sense of energy and anticipation he used to feel at the beginning of a day's hunting. He challenged the whole day to come by singing heartily around the house, "Praise God from whom all blessings flow!" — his signal for the remainder of the household to rise and assemble for prayers.

They all gathered around the oak table. Elizabeth snivelled with a cold, while William tried to wake up his drowsy children with an energetic psalm. As he read a lesson and then a prayer, John and Jane slowly overcame their daze. Finally, as always, William blessed his family fervently as if he might never see them again: "God bless you in your souls and in your bodies and all you put your hand to this day, and whether you live or die the Lord grant that you may live or die to Him." Then they had breakfast. Molly sat with them, for William carelessly allowed privileges to the servant although Elizabeth did not like it and resisted by deliberately giving her orders the moment that she sat down. At eight o'clock the church bell chimed — thirteen times, to tell the villagers that this was the thirteenth day of the month. At half-past eight Grimshaw walked to his vestry ahead of his family. Dozens of robins, thrushes and blackbirds were now singing around the town whilst hundreds more could be heard fading into the distance and larks screamed in the air as he followed a path from Sowdens made of slabs of stone and laid by Isaac Smith. It stretched half a mile down the slope, and before pitching into the valley of the Bridgehouse Beck it turned left to reach the west end of the church. William turned a corner where the cold blew more savagely — in every hundred yards of West Yorkshire there is such a corner — then came into the shelter of trees and entered his church that was still tingling with the smell of brimstone.

Whilst Jonathan Whitehead smirked and fussed, Grimshaw bore himself like an emperor robing for his court. The two men could hear from outside a gradually increasing cacophony of barking dogs, horses' neighing, clattering hooves and the shouting and joking of people who had not met for a week and were arguing about whose horse was to be grazed where in the churchyard. Some of them had travelled a dozen miles over the bogs to enjoy the hot company of a crowd and perhaps also to make a sly sale of a beast, a corner of land or a piece of cloth, before they listened to the parson telling them what news from Spain had arrived by the stage coach, and then to snooze through the rest of his proceedings. All the inns were busy, offering stabling and a quick nip of brandy for everyone before they faced — alas! — the sermon threatened by the new pulpit. A stink of horses came in through the vestry door and with it, too, the occasional shouted hope that the sermon would be a short one.

William knew when his own family arrived because of a sudden lull in the noise. The churchwardens parted the crowds to make a way to their pew, just below the pulpit. A faint mist rose above the congregation. Elizabeth, suffering from a cold, felt suffocated by the stink of sheep, cattle and sweat that came off the pale-faced weavers and woolcombers. Jane had been told the story of Jonah and she saw the dark nave of the church, with the ribs of oak curving up to the ceiling, as the huge stomach of a whale that had swallowed her. The smell made it seem even more like a stomach. She entered the family's new pew (a shining brass plaque with their name on it newly fastened to its side) with pride — it was like trying on a new dress! As soon as the Grimshaw family knelt and prayed, disappearing below the lip of the oak stall, they were forgotten by the crowd that for a moment had stared so insolently and brutally.

The noise quietened again when William entered. He spent sometime circulating in the nave like a farmer at a market, red-faced from being out of doors, bluff, blunt and seeking an advantage everywhere as he chatted. Then his face lost that saintly gloss and as was his way he unexpectedly showed his ferocious side. He had seen dogs running around the church and he began to kick them out. The country people laughed and helped with the sport, relieved that their new parson was such good fun.

When William mounted his pulpit, the row still continued. Jonathan Whitehead, thinking nothing of it — a good parson with a powerful voice could make himself heard — came to the foot of the pulpit and blew his pitch-pipe to set the note of the tune to which the first psalm would be chanted. The crowd that had been so excited now began a dreary dirge, resentful of the next hour's boredom before they could go to the inn, then home for a meal, a sleep in front of the fire and finally attend to their farm stock. William read out his document of conformity to the Thirty-Nine Articles of the Church of England, as the law required. No-one was interested and he could not be heard over the rustling and the noise. He glared over the church. You could feel it in the air that the parson and his congregation were now challenging one another. Almost anything could ignite their animosity to his altar rail, his new font, and the lofty position he had given himself high up in the black oak pulpit.

Somebody at the back began very quietly to stamp his heavy boots. Someone else picked up the rhythm, and another person, then another. It grew louder, spreading along pew after pew. First the men, then the women. They had obviously used this barbaric music before to make someone unwelcome. They stared the new parson in the face, whilst their noise grew steadily louder. The brass plate and the candle holders rattled; it was as if it was intended to shake down the church tower. Grimshaw's family and friends in the front pews were embarrassed and fidgety, but the parson's only expression was a disgusted twitching of the corner of his mouth. His implacability, in the end, defeated the congregation. The stamping faded. The horses in the graveyard, the dogs that had been cleared out to run around in a yelping pack and the curlews on the moors could be heard quite clearly. A smell of smoke and an occasional glitter of fires as the breeze caught them on the moors could be seen through the door. Grimshaw's calmness was more disturbing than if he had been angry with them. He roared that he would not go on with the service until they had all stooped to their knees and begged God for forgiveness of their sins. Those in the front pews obeyed instantly, but the people behind wavered. A surprised sigh passed through other pews, like a breeze through a field of grass, dying in silence. There was a clatter of phials of sal volatile from some of the ladies; coughing, the scraping of feet, tutting. As Grimshaw held the silence, more and more people fell to their knees and he led their prayers. Then he calmly made his announcements — the symptoms of a virulent cattle-disease, and news of the King's army in Spain.

Grimshaw's sermon followed, and it stunned them. With flat Lancashire vowels, he yelled at them and waved like a man driving cattle through a gate. "We 'umans are nowt but a mass of animated filth and must cry t' 'Eaven to be forgiven for our sins!" he roared. "Man may calculate to t'minute an eclipse that'll 'appen in five hundred years. But does he know what changes may take place in the next day or hour in his nearest concern? Does he? He measures the earth and weighs the air and numbers the stars. But whilst he prides himself on his excursions abroad, he is a stranger at 'ome. Vain man, who would be deemed wise though he is ignorant as the wild ass's colt, presumes to have control of himself!'' Mad Grimshaw's voice rose to a crescendo on the word "himself". He thumped the pulpit and his massive gowns tilted sideways, like a man-of-war turning to bear down on them, its sails filled with wind. He cast his big round glaring eye slowly along the pews, like an angler trawling his bait over the bed of a stream and watching for a fish to bite. "God made man in His own image and likeness, but from Adam's disobedience came alienation from God! Cast into t' wilderness o' *this* world, man can do nothing but evil before God! However good and virtuous he seems, he's deserving of *nowt but eternal burning! We are born in sin and must ever dwell in it!''* His voice rose again, cracking slightly and terrifying. People saw his eyes and teeth glowing above his black garments. The smell of brimstone lingering in the church made them think they were already in Hell.

Jane, sunk in the pew below her father as if in a pit, could see only the tip of his black and white hawk-like form perched above. Ruffling his gowns, he seemed about to fly off amongst the rafters. But he too must burn for ever for his sins, so why was *he* not frightened? Her brother John didn't seem to care either. Imitating the villagers banging their clogs, he kicked his legs against the pew until his stepmother stopped him, whereupon he tried to do it silently, resting his chin on the pew front and insolently staring at everyone, interested in their warts and goitres. Jonas Appleyard looked as nervous as a lamb smelling blood at the door of a slaughterhouse. Others of the churchwardens had benign satisfied expressions, as if they had drunk too much brandy.

The silence in the church seemed to turn into a solid substance, a grey heavy thing like a wet woollen coat. Everyone tried to remember something that might be a sin — some half-stifled memory because of which he was now unable to look his relatives and friends in the face. Little Jane recalled that she had been unwilling to get out of bed for prayers at five o'clock this Sunday morning. A man who on his way home from the wool-traders' hall in Bradford with the payment for a week or more's work by his family, had stopped "for a

44

moment" at an inn, stayed for three days and spent everything, now did not dare lift his blushing head from his pew: the orange and purple flames of Hell roared inside his head. Women who remembered kisses given too willingly at the end of long summer evenings, when they left their spinning wheels to help with the harvest, now expected to be damned for ever. Forgetting that Grimshaw had not mentioned any sins in particular, they all felt that the parson knew the intimate details of the life of each one of them. Women especially felt their insides crumbling, as if they were in the presence of God Himself. A soft fatalistic snivelling was heard out of the dark belly of the church.

As soon as he had cast everyone down, Grimshaw gave them hope. "Are we completely lost?" he cried. He modulated his great voice to a warbling tremolo and it became as soft as if he was stroking a kitten. "No! No! For God sent His Son into t' world! This Jesus is our only Saviour and Redeemer! By faith in Christ are men justified! Have faith and thalt *know* theeself redeemed! Faith is the gift of God!"

Under the strain some people began to weep. A few of the gentry in the front pew now decided that they had suffered enough of being brow-beaten by the sheer nonsense of an enthusiastic parson and, red-faced with anger, they left noisily. A sniggering and whispering broke out, but most people did not dare to turn their heads. William Grimshaw silently watched the departure. Through the faint nervous shuffling that began to grow amongst children and incontinent old people, he completed his sermon.

When William had finished, a relieved stamping of feet broke out. The horses, which were used to much shorter services, recognised the end at last and whinnied excitedly. The beggars and old soldiers crouching by the north wall now moved round to the west door. But many of the most pious people, those most likely to make gifts to the poor, stayed to take Communion at the changed altar rail, to pray, even to weep. As they came back dazed from the dark regions of the spirit they felt for a few moments deserted because Grimshaw had left the nave. Hardly anyone dared look another person in the face.

In the church porch, Thomas Pighells, already slightly drunk, thrust the beggars to one side and shouted, "He preached us to Hell and left us there! Is that the way for t' parson to carry on?"

William appeared with the step of a conqueror. "That is the best cat which catches the most mice," he smoothly answered. Then he astounded them by walking home with his family instead of going to the inn with the trustees as the parson usually did, and where over a glass of brandy they hoped to tell him how a parson ought to behave.

Chapter 4

MOST PEOPLE LEFT the church noisily and excitedly but there was
one young man whom the experience plunged into silence. This was
Paul Greenwood, whose father John Greenwood was a churchwarden and becoming Grimshaw's closest friend. Paul was eighteen
years old and apparently destined like his father to be a master
clothier, a man who contemplatively sucked grasses plucked from
his new enclosures and the proprietor of a countryside that spun and
wove his wool and filled his barns with hay. But Paul would rather
read sermons than concern himself with trade. He often sneaked
across the moors before daybreak to join Dissenters who met in
cowsheds to listen to preaching carpenters, stonemasons and tailors.
These had led Paul to that same literature to which Grimshaw was
addicted and which emphasised our abject dependence upon God.

Paul's face was shining with revelation today as he left the church.
He was silent almost the whole way home to Ponden Hall, in a gig
with his parents, his brother and sister. Paul sat on the back seat, no-
one troubling him because they were used to him not speaking. His
head was bent over his closed prayer book. His lips were tense and
the muscles twitched in his face. The others crowded in front of him
were telling each other repeatedly that Grimshaw was the kind of
strong parson needed for these God-forsaken moors, whilst the
horses trotted for five miles along the upper part of the Worth
Valley. In Stanbury they suddenly could not see where they were
going for smoke pouring off the moor. This produced un-Sabbatical
giggles from maids and gardeners huddling together in their gig, but
Paul didn't turn a hair. Now the valley narrowed, the river crashed
over rocks and swirled into deep pools under rowans. They saw the
sun brilliantly for a moment, crashing onto the banks of spring
flowers, wood anemones, celandines, and upon the bright green
grass. Paul merely dipped his head firmly down towards his Bible
and his prayer book.

They came to Ponden Hall, which was at the joining point of two
small brooks that tumbled out of the moors as if excited to escape

from them. In the yard everyone descended quickly to get into the house for dinner. A good sermon put as keen an edge on folks' appetites as a morning's hunting! Paul still kept apart, and instead of going into the house he sneaked off following the boy who led the horses into the stable. From there a doorway led into the barn where he went alone. The building was dark, warm, dry and muffled in the maternal forms of mounds of straw and hay. Shafts of glittering light pierced like knives through thin lancet windows. Hens scratched peacefully and a calf sniffed the hay.

"Oh to be rid of the bitterness of sin! Oh to be saved from lust!" Paul thought. Surrendering to the weakness in his knees he knelt down in the straw and chaff and he prayed. "Oh to be able to give myself to God, free of trade and the farm!"

Paul's father John Greenwood shouted in the yard. Paul only half heard and he took no notice. He was so still that the calf came over to look at him, its gawky legs stiffened and ready to bolt, its ears erect. As he opened the great door of the barn John Greenwood's figure seemed to melt in the swamp of light. His angry shout was stifled in his throat, for his son looked so vulnerable and for an instant reminded him of himself at the age of eighteen — before the skin of his cheeks fattened, sagged, grew red and leathery and before his expression hardened with trade — so that it made him catch his breath. This moment of recognition took him unawares, and then seemed never to have quite existed, like spring sunlight fading off the grass. He scratched his wig in doubt. John Greenwood had been impressed from the beginning by William Grimshaw — it was Greenwood who had suggested that the Todmorden curate be invited to Haworth after talking to John Lockwood at the cloth halls in Heptonstall, Halifax and Bradford — and he had welcomed Grimshaw by giving him a strong brown cob for him to ride over his big, wild parish. But today was the first time he had heard the parson preach and, he had to confess, he did sound a bit too enthusiastic. Now Grimshaw's relentless message poured back into his head. The blurred memories of a thousand suppressed sins rose up to choke him like a late supper of cheese and pickles — the thousand little offences against God that any man of forty engaged in trade has had to commit. He crept over to Paul and knelt wordlessly beside him whilst the calf frisked off towards the barn door — with huge sinless eyes it stared, then bolted into the yard, joining the swallows and the butterflies. Paul prayed aloud thanking God for this miracle that had brought his father to his side. John Greenwood remembered the parson's words: that only deep, deep repentance could hope to turn aside the gates of wrath. He was a strong and sober man but he began to tremble in fear that his repentance might not be enough to save him from everlasting burning.

Outside fat Mrs Greenwood was furious at a spoiled dinner and shouting, "John! Paul!". She was ungainly everywhere outside kitchen and drawing room, and she stumbled irritably amongst the obstacles of the farmyard, the ruts, drains, uneven cobbles and piles of manure. Seeing the barn door left open she came in shouting, but she stopped, speechless, when she saw husband and son kneeling and muttering. She too had from the beginning been in favour of introducing a strong parson to control the weavers and woolcombers, but in the event had been troubled in a way she had not expected by Mad Grimshaw's first sermon. Though she had chattered ceaselessly about his looks, particularly the mad roll of his eyes, about his dead wife buried in Luddenden and about the stuck-up lady he had next married; although she had disapproved of his vulgar accent, his farmer's dress and his manner of thumping the edge of the pulpit fit to break it, yet she remained disturbed. Grimshaw had put a frown on her face and she had tried ever since to find fault with everyone. When her husband, hardly interrupting his prayers, motioned her to kneel beside him, her need of forgiveness, her fear of death snatching her away unforgiven, overwhelmed her. She knelt, praying to be washed clean so that Grace might descend, and seeing all the time the black-gowned parson rising before her just as if she was still in church.

Half an hour later Paul's brother and sister appeared. Martha Greenwood had hardly stopped giggling since she nearly burst her bladder during the long sermon, but when she saw her parents, her giggling seized up and she suddenly thought, "What if I be taken this instant off to Hell with my sins unforgiven?" and she went to join them. Her brother William, a big simple lad who best enjoyed being with animals, came into the barn, opened his mouth wide at what he saw, but thinking that his father, his mother, his sister and his brother must be right, without quite knowing what he was doing, went across and knelt with them. The family group seemed as hopeless as if the Day of Judgement was on them already. John Greenwood's knees ached but he felt unable to move. William itched but dared not scratch himself. Then something strange happened to

49

Paul. His lips trembling, his eyes shining, he whispered ecstatically, "I'm saved! I'm saved!" The same ecstasy overcame the others. First they whispered and then shouted. When they came out of the barn, with a radiance like Grimshaw's upon their faces, the world seemed even to smell differently and more sweetly to them. The calf, quivering on its stalk-like legs, stood still to watch them, its head tilted slightly to one side. Then it gave up wondering about the strange antics of humans because of their fear of eternity and turned to the comfort of its mother, who lay like a dappled boulder in the grass.

Scenes of this kind happened all over the parish. Women whose husbands were away at the wars and who had been struggling alone between cowshed and loom, worrying about the sickness of their babies and about their husbands in Spain, were answered with the message of this powerful stranger. Their knees gave way in moorland lanes as they walked home, in the back rooms of inns and by manure heaps as they cleaned out cowshed or stable.

At noon, Grimshaw ate beef and drank wine. His wife, more than ever after the scene in the church, felt a mixture of both fear and pride in him. She put her feelings to the test, challenging her husband by sending the servant into the kitchen just as she was preparing to sit with them. Grimshaw raised his hand, said that Molly was to stay, and that was that.

Later, instead of taking a nap William went for a stroll, more to check on Sabbath breakers than expecting to discover a revival of religion in his parish. In his own village there was the noise of profane laughter. A group of men and boys were hanging a dog for stealing meat. The men shuffled when Grimshaw appeared whilst the dog convulsed and squealed on its rope, its half-dead eyes bulging like grey bottle-glass. Grimshaw ordered them to cut it down and hang it on Monday. He asked each one if he had been confirmed. "Aye, I'm telled it's a good cure for rheumatism," one answered insolently. At this Grimshaw had them all kneeling and saying the Lord's Prayer in the street.

Next, he heard fiddle music in a house. As he came close he could hear the stamping of boots in a jig. Without knocking he entered the passageway, the timbers of the floor creaking above him. He climbed upstairs, which was dark and smelling of tobacco — the walls and ceiling were stained with it. Most of the people there did not know the parson. They were Irish Catholics, whole families of whom brought their scythes to Yorkshire to mow the grass, moving on hire from farm to farm across the county. But the air of the man in the doorway and the way in which one or two present said "Parson Grimshaw!" caused the music and the dancing to trickle to a standstill. William Grimshaw, furious, went up to the fiddler, snatched hold of the instrument, put it over his knee, broke it and threw the pieces down on the floor. The pathetic fiddler, his hand shaking, scratched the back of his head with an absurdly casual gesture. Before he understood what had happened to him, Grimshaw had left and had set off again across the fields and commons.

It was a lovely spring afternoon, although misted by the smoke from the moors — it rolled off in great dark fleeces and draped the town with a thin veil which had tainted clothes with its smell for several weeks now so that nobody took notice of it. On the moors the larks called shrilly as they darted over their destroyed nests, but lower down when sunlight fell upon a patch of grass, a lark arose from it more calmly and sang God's praises. In the fields the flowers also praised Him — if this were not their purpose, Grimshaw reasoned, doubtless the Lord would have prevented their strivings in sky and earth on Sunday. The fine weather had brought people out. Boys and girls were playing "tiggy" around a stone column until William stopped and catechised them. Other children were setting fire to grass on the edges of the common. Farmers were astonished at the nimble way Grimshaw scrambled over walls and nipped between rows of cloth. He appeared suddenly, walking through fire, or out of a cloud of smoke — smuts of burnt grass and heather clinging to his black clothes — to ask them if they were in church that morning. "He darts about like a man that's lost a calf," one said. Many had come out to avoid the wailings of wife, sisters and daughters — for it was mostly the women who were emotional about Grimshaw's preaching — and they grabbed him in the hope that he would "cure" their families. Instead, Mad Grimshaw would not leave until the man himself had knelt with the women.

The parson was aiming for a disused quarry which John Greenwood had told him was used as a courting place, even on Sundays. Anybody but Grimshaw going there only to peep and pry would have been stoned. Most of the couples lay behind boulders but from the

51

top of the quarry Grimshaw could see them all. The girls lying on their backs were the first to spot him. Boys experiencing an unexpected coitus interruptus or seeing the dazed eyes of their petted maidens fill with shock, and feeling hands that should have caressed them instead begin roughly to straighten their clothes, turned to look at the hole of Heaven above the quarry where they saw the parson. A few leapt up, instinctively grasping stones in their hands, but quickly changing their minds. More ran away instantly, shouting, "It's t'new parson! Quick!"

William stared without speaking for several minutes, pinning one lover after another with his eye. In the basin of the quarry, a big sixteen year old lad, red-faced with adolescent awkwardness and boisterous as a puppy, was one minute pummelling a girl and the next hanging onto her neck and kissing her. The girl struggled free to stand a few feet away, her eyes shining, tempting him to come and handle her some more. Then she ran a few feet further. "Michael! Michael Beever, leave me alone!" she laughed. They were like animals playing. He pulled her into the grass. She held her skirt down, but then she gave in. She became calm, her skirt lifted over her face, the boy pumping above her. She stood up, almost casually straightening her dress and brushing aside her long blonde hair from her face and shoulders. Her hair was roughly washed and untrimmed. Patches of cow dung clung to her ankles, her cotton dress, her breast. She blushed as at last she caught Grimshaw's eye — he was thinking that she was exceptionally beautiful.

William clambered down the quarry slopes. Whilst he was hidden behind blocks of stone at a few turns of the path, some more couples dashed away. A few boys, stranded in the basin of the quarry, looked foxily in all directions whilst others put on bold faces, with their fists clenched. Grimshaw intended to take down names and hold interviews later at Sowdens. Firstly he went up to the brazen couple in the centre, and it was the girl who answered him: "Sally Rushworth. Sir," with a mocking curtsy.

Sally's father, Ben Rushworth, was the elected "clerk" of the semi-secret Haworth Union Society. At first sight Ben was not striking as a radical leader. He was small and thin with his chest caved in from stooping over a hot and fuming woolcombing pot. Like most woolcombers he had a cough which turned to bronchitis every winter and spring. He was perhaps more sly than brave, yet his integrity in following radical causes was such that many prophesied he would live to be hanged. From the first words he spoke you would think he had reason to be bitter, and yet he did not seem to be so. He had loved his children unusually but three of them had died in Haworth's regular plagues of typhoid fever and he learnt then that no-one could really help him ever. As a child Ben had attended the school that Isaac Smith's daughter had kept in an abandoned dairy. He learnt to read from an alphabet that the mason had carved on the back of a tombstone and set up in the schoolroom. After the Bible, Ben progressed to Plato and Isaac Newton, and he usually worked with one of these propped up near his comb-pot.

Ben's ideas of political justice were plucked mostly from his Bible: the margin and fly-leaves were full of annotations. As a young man he had turned to the religious sects — mainly Baptist, Presbyterian and Quaker. These held discussions about equality, justice, and the day when the world would end, to be followed by the reign of happiness for poor people. Did man need a master? Them royalty down London, with lumps of white vermin skins hanging round their necks, Ben wondered? There was evidently no need for clergy, for amongst Dissenters the preaching was done by anyone who had something to say and who for the rest of the week laboured with his hands.

Even more was discussed in the local woolcombers' shop where half a dozen craftsmen worked together. Woolcombers travelled the country to pick up work and they were organised into a guild, so Ben's shop was often visited by strangers. Locals also dropped in to sit on a bench as if the place was a public house and chat, discuss politics, or have a Bible passage expounded. It was a warm place to be in winter — "As warm as Hell," the wives said. The stove glowed under the comb-pot and the apprentices were sent out continually to fetch ale. At this university of the woolcombing shop, ideas melted and fused together in Ben's mind like iron in a blacksmith's forge. Ben heard of the Yorkshire Grindletonians who said that if Paradise was not achieved on earth it would not be attained at all. Someone told Ben that working men were enlisted to fight foreign wars in order to bleed them from their own causes in England. He heard of James Naylor, a fellow-Yorkshireman who wrote that God "made all men of one mould and one blood to dwell on the face of the earth". Cromwell's government flogged Naylor, branded him, pilloried him and bored a hole through his tongue for saying such things. Ben was told that property was the original cause of sin. Gerard Winstanley was quoted: "All your particular churches are like the enclosure of land which hedges in some to be heirs of life and hedges out others. . . . True religion and undefiled is to let everyone quietly have earth to manure." Ben became the circus master of a wild menagerie of opinions, but above all Winstanley became his hero, and with the Reverend Isaac Smith's connivance he had the quotation pinned to the church door.

Ben realised that for such activities he would be kept for ever at the level of a journeyman-woolcomber — the master clothiers would see to it that he never amassed the capital nor received the trade to run his own shop. He felt stranded in Haworth and thought of going to London, but he loved his wife Mercy and daughter Sally too dearly to leave them. He knew that a man could not have a better wife and his greatest worry was that he might not be a good enough husband for her. He often came home drunk with righteous anger and he tried to instruct his wife and daughter in his politics. But Mercy Rushworth was afraid of such things being mentioned, even in private. "Walls have ears," she said. Ben, melting with love and tenderness, promised to express his ideas no more. However, realising that there remained no further outlets for his ambition and talents, he resolved to devote his life to the local Union Society.

The Society seemed inoffensive, its declared aims being charity and insurance. The members contributed a penny each week as a premium against the death of the main wage-earner in the family. It also acted as a bank in which money was saved for annual trips to the Bishop Blaize festivities in Bradford. (Bishop Blaize, who had been martyred with hot combs, was the patron saint of woolcombers. There was a fair and a procession of woolstaplers, woolcombers, woolsorters and charcoal burners on caparisoned horses, and with tableaux showing shepherds and shepherdesses, and shepherds and swains mounted on carts.) You did not seem compelled to hold radical opinions to qualify for membership of Haworth Union Society, nor did you have to be a woolcomber. Only reasonably good health was demanded (you could not join if you had venereal disease, or had been injured through fighting) and sober habits; you were refused if you had been convicted of felony, confined in a jail, frequented gaming houses, swore, or were addicted to intoxicating liquor. Yet every wool-master knew that if there was trouble amongst the weavers and the woolcombers, the Union Society was at the bottom of it. And why did the Union refuse membership to anyone who voluntarily joined the army? It meant that they would not have those whose political reliability was suspect. Then there was their interest in books. That was always suspicious. They had their own book club — a sub-committee who subscribed an extra few pence each week to buy volumes. Any travelling member made it his business to call in at other branches of the Woolcombers' Society, to exchange books with them or buy at their auctions. This way Ben had purchased Pope's *Homer* for eight shillings, and for four shillings a 1724 edition of *The History of the Conquest of Mexico by the Spaniards.*

The inner committee of the Union used to meet in semi-secret in an upstairs room of the inn, with the shutters closed and a scout posted at the foot of the stairs whilst they discussed philosophy, physics, astronomy and the classics. And the general drift of these subjects — particularly in the hands of passionate self-educated working men, who rolled all topics into one in their discussions — was, as everyone knew, towards the overthrow of governments; especially when discussed in a fug of tobacco smoke and beer.

On the afternoon of Grimshaw's stroll, the committee was in session to initiate a man named John Shread as a new member. Shread was short, physically vigorous, with a straw-coloured halo of light hair that was for ever rising about his head in the breeze. Only two weeks previously he had visited the new parson to tell him that by tradition he had a right to the grass in the churchyard in return for his wife and himself making rush-lights for the church. Shread owned three looms and appeared then to be ambitious of becoming a church trustee. Now here he was at the Union Society! The room where they met was twilit, with only cracks of light through the shutters and from the flames of a couple of rush-lights. Shread was blindfolded and as helpless as a nestling. He could hear the typically heavy breathing and coughing of woolcombers and he felt the presences of maybe a dozen people around him. With his hands behind his back, Shread was marched quickly and firmly several times around the room until he didn't know where he was. Meanwhile the men sitting against the wall began a weird, primitive banging on sheets of iron. This strange noise carried right across Haworth and it was the only part of the ceremony known to everyone. Women at the wells caught their breath whilst the children sniggered and made obscene mimes to one another: they told one another that the wool-combers cut off one another's testicles.

Just as Shread was about to collapse with dizziness, the noise stopped and he was brought to rest. Someone took off the blindfold. Shread's cheeks were twitching with fear. In the yellow rush-lights he saw painted on the wall before him (and obviously executed by the same hand that made the sign for the inn) a life-size skeleton. It was labelled DEATH. A sword was suspended above it and underneath an inscription, REMEMBER THY END. A Bible stood on the floor. All the members now began stamping with their iron-shod clogs, just as they had done at Grimshaw's sermon. Suddenly, after about three minutes, the rhythm stopped. Shread had not yet dared to look around, when a voice from behind that he half-recognised as Ben Rushworth's ordered him to kneel. So he knelt and placed his hands upon the Bible. Then he took an oath: "I call upon God to witness this my solemn oath that nothing, no not death itself, shall make me give information respecting anything in this Lodge, and that if I should violate this my solemn oath then may my soul be burnt in the lowest pit of Hell to all eternity".

Then Shread was turned to face everyone. He saw Jim O't'Moor Gate, looking solemn for the first time ever he'd seen, because normally he was fooling and playing his fiddle at fairs and wakes and inns, his bright red hair tossing about to the storm of his music; and Bill O't'Cows, named after his father who'd possessed some though Bill ruined himself selling broadsheets and pamphlets amongst people who were incapable of reading them; and a dozen others whom Shread knew. They looked so woe-faced that Shread almost burst into laughter. He was on his way upwards to prosperity and he now wondered why he had come here. The committee cleared their throats and spat their phlegm. Ben Rushworth sternly brought them to order and they chanted together verses from chapter 21 of the Book of Ezekiel:

Sigh, therefore, thou son of man, with the breaking of thy loins; and with bitterness sigh before their eyes. . . . Son of man, prophesy, and say, Thus saith the Lord; Say, a sword, a sword is sharpened, and also furbished that it may glitter; should we then make mirth? . . . Cry and howl, son of man: for it shall be upon my people, it shall be upon all the princes of Israel: terrors by reason of the sword shall be upon my people . . . I will overturn,

overturn, overturn, it: and it shall be no more, until he comes whose right it is; and I will give it him . . . The sword, the sword is drawn: for the slaughter it is furbished, to consume because of the glittering . . .

People in the street tried to head Grimshaw off, but neither they nor the scout at the door could prevent his bursting in. Even he was dumbfounded by the strange prayer meeting, held in semi-darkness in a smell of rush-lights and tobacco, with a crude painting of Death on the wall. There, too, was a piece of the old font which was supposedly broken up and used to fill pot-holes after it was taken from the church. The fragment showed a winged griffin, used here probably for witchcraft. There was a silence when Grimshaw entered. He slowly, deliberately, picked up a volume that lay on a table. It was entitled, *An Enquiry into the Natural Rights of Mankind to Debate Freely concerning Religion, by A Gentleman of Lincolns Inn 1737.*

Shread shuffled his feet. Ben turned to confront the parson, but Grimshaw let his own rage loose first. "These are acts of witchcraft and sorcery deserving the attention of the ecclesiastical courts!" Meanwhile the Haworth Union Society studied their man. Ben Rushworth calmly opened the shutters and all the mystery of the room was dispelled by the light of the smoky early summer afternoon, the view of green hills where curlews were calling.

"They do say that a time will be when God will come amongst men and scatter the rich man's gold around in the streets," Ben said.

"The only way we will grow rich is by the progress of trade and of the King's foreign wars," Grimshaw growled.

"And happy? What about that cause? I'm told that you were once cheerful when you were at Cambridge — and even after that." Ben's Yorkshire accent had a relaxed and rich quality like dark velvet, nevertheless his words were always blunt without his even realising that it was so. Grimshaw felt a stab of conscience about his student days and his half-forgotten joy with Sarah; having God's work to do now he could not bear the reminder. "Happiness comes only from God!" he shouted uselessly, to hide his feelings.

"And sometimes from the Devil! For some, such as those who are coming into Yorkshire today, all pleasure, even the most honest, has to feel as though it is tainted with sin and therefore to be kept secret before they can enjoy it. Thus the simplest things such as music are turned into a vice — for those who cannot gain anything from it otherwise. And I dread what is going to happen to our Yorkshiremen because of this,'' Ben prophesied, and added, ''Besides, even God cannot bring happiness to a man whose belly isn't filled.''

Thus with a sincere desire for knowledge, and lucidly, although they pronounced names and terms wrongly, the thin-chested workmen faced the corpulent parson. Nobody had ever talked so clearly to William before. He stammered. He was defeated. And the Union Society, strangers to Grimshaw and without knowledge of the turmoiled depths of his mind, decided from their point of view that outside theological and legal subjects, this Bachelor of Arts from Cambridge was shallow and intellectually unsatisfying.

Chapter 5

WHEN GRIMSHAW HAD been in Haworth for a year or so, a Scotsman named William Darney appeared in the West Riding. He was a
good-looking rough man, thirty-seven years of age, huge, with a big
red beard and hair. He rented a farm at Miller's Barn in Bacup, sixteen miles from Haworth. Every now and then, sometimes most
inconveniently in the middle of haymaking or when the earth was
right for ploughing, he would, instead of working, brood over his
Bible or Bunyan, composing verses, muttering them to himself but
hardly speaking to anyone else except to burst like gunfire into
expounding a passage that moved him — usually from Revelation or
Daniel, such as, "Babylon is fallen, is fallen, that great city".
Darney's own barns and outbuildings were in ruins so that when his
family entered to feed the beasts they ran out again quickly in case
the whole building collapsed. The prophet used to walk about
muttering some of his several hundred verses about the struggle to
convert Yorkshire and Lancashire, for he knew that apart from the
work of a few preachers such as Grimshaw, the north of England
was barbarous and godless. He would rise in the middle of the night
and sleep during the day. The cyclical recurrences of his religion were
like a woman's menstruation, which disrupted his metabolism.

"The poor will inherit the earth," he said thoughtfully.

His ten-year-old son, struggling with a rebellious flock of geese,
ducks and a goat, understood that "the poor" were themselves.
"When?" he asked, meaning, would it be for Christmas or for his
birthday?

"Soon," Darney said. " 'Tis prophesied and we must be
prepared."

When he could no longer resist the call to preach, he would pack a
bag with his Bible, prayer book and with bits of lace, bobbins, handkerchiefs, crude perfumes and almanacs containing prophecies to
sell to servant girls. (Preaching and pedling — natural partners —
had brought him from Scotland.) He was a cobbler too, and he
packed his last, awl and spools of thread. He was likely to be away

for from one to three months, leaving the care of his farm and two babies to his wife and his ten-year-old son. Mrs Darney was jealous because at many of the places William went to he was entertained by "Darney Societies", who were mostly women. By curing a sick cow or prophesying a cloudburst he had "proved" to them that he was the Messiah who would appear again at the Second Coming, after a flood or a storm, when peace and love would then reign on earth for ever. Darney had a regular circuit between Bacup, Todmorden, Hebden Bridge, Heptonstall, Haworth, Nelson and Burnley, from which he often stepped out of the way to convert fresh villages. Sometimes he began by displaying his wares, at other times he started chatting to the children or the women, and occasionally he began preaching immediately, taking out his Bible at a fair or amongst people with little else to do but listen to him whilst they grazed their cow or geese on a common. He was known everywhere in the district. The children first, then the women, lastly the surly and suspicious men would come to be amused by his turn of metaphor, or more likely to throw stones. Darney had never applied to protect himself with a dissenting preacher's licence. His habits were too irregular, and he was never downcast by his sufferings, having lots of sharp answers for his enemies and his fists flying. In the end, his safety, like a fly's, lay in his restlessness.

One Sunday in November 1745 Darney arrived in Hebden Bridge. It was raining hard and a great many people had left the town. They had gone either to Bradford or to Halifax — that is, as near as they dared go to Wakefield and Leeds, to find out about the rumour that an advance guard of the Scottish Pretender's army had come to ask for ransoms, demanding for instance £40,000 from the City of York. Nevertheless a good crowd turned out for Darney, either because he was the nearest they could get to a Scots rebel, or just for the fun. A woman provided Darney with an upturned wash-tub to stand on. Before beginning, he hitched up his clothes, licked his thumb and spat on his palms like a workman about to start a job, or an uneducated man opening a book. The rain flooded off his great hat and his leather clothes gleamed with wet.

"My dear brethren!" he roared. "We live in an age of slavery, of raising money by lotteries, of theatres and other places of idle amusement! With nobility who live at ease lusting after novelty, spending their time singing and indulging filthy and ungodly conversation! Merchants engage in extravagant merchandising —"

"What's yon Scots Papist selling? Almanacs and lace, isn't it?"

"— possessing property and laying house to house, field to field and one village to another, taking away the common rights of the poor and not suffering them to glean in the enclosures. Like the lords of creation they go horse-racing, hunting, wrestling. They go to fairs and bear baitings or play at cards. Justices take away our rights and fail to deliver the poor from his oppressor. But I tell you the day will come when Christ will reign in glory and wealth will be taken from the rich and given to the poor, when the gates of Heaven will be open and every man will be given at least forty acres of land! Praise be to God for his mercy!"

The crowd liked this. Then Darney described the experiences that had brought him to the Lord, which bored them, so that he had to shout. When he was nine years old, he said, his father's reading of the twentieth chapter of Revelation — "And I saw an angel come down from heaven, having the key of the bottomless pit and a great chain in his hand. And he laid hold on the dragon, that old serpent, which is the devil, and Satan, and bound him a thousand years" — filled William with such a sense of guilt that he fell face downwards to the floor, screaming and weeping. At the age of sixteen he had dreamed of Jeremiah thrown, because of his prophesying, on the dung heap where butchers poured offal and blood. But he was so happy there that William wanted to change places with him as the way to cure his sins. As a young man he had been so much in danger of falling into "scandalous sins" that he had prayed twenty times a day for the Lord to give him a wife.

"Your doctrine is fine but it would sound better in a church!" someone shouted.

"If a man was hungry in the midst of a desert and wholesome food were brought to him, he would not refuse to eat because he was not in a dining room!" Darney answered.

"Thart right! Thart right! Good food is good wherever it's eaten!" they replied, amused.

The audience was again interested in what he had to say, so he ceased to shout. "When we fall into the gulf of God's judgement it will be into a place without flowers or grass or clear streams, and lit by the flames of sulphur burning in the cauldrons of the valleys!" he said, pointing to the black slippery-looking moors seeping with water.

61

Bored by evangelism once again, the crowd began to clap rhythmically:

> "Here comes the Methodee parson
> Here comes the ranter bold
> He kissed my wife . . ."

"Papist!" someone shouted. "Scotch Will the Jacobite! No Popery! Vicar's coming to arrest thee! Tha's disturbed his Sunday sermon. He'll kill thee!"

"He must ask my Father's leave first. For if He has work for me to do, all the men in town cannot hinder me until I have done it. Praised be the Lord for his mercy." Darney had a habit of winking one eye slowly when he had a witty answer.

"Put him in the army to fight the Jacobites!"

Some of the soaked crowd drifted away, but the others were arriving, beating a drum and wheeling a barrel of ale on a cart. A way was made for this to reach the foot of Darney's wash-tub. "Free beer from t' vicar!" a huge miller shouted to the crowd. "And I charge thee in the name of King George to come down!" the miller said to the preacher.

"I charge thee in the name of the King of Kings to let me get on wi' my sermon!" Darney answered. "Bless the Lord for my delivery!"

The woman who had provided the wash-tub held tightly onto Darney's pedlar's pack and turned her eyes from her master to his enemies, unanswerable sarcasms lying too timid for utterance on her lips. Eggs, turnips and fireworks that mostly fizzled out in the rain had been thrown desultorily at him all morning without shifting him from his tub. But now some young men came with a willow branch that had been dipped in a cesspool and they pushed it into his face. This toppled him from his pedestal. A strong young fellow tore Darney's coat from him and disappeared into Hebden Bridge, shouting, "We're baitin' Scotch Will! We're baitin' Scotch Will!" Some tried to get hold of his pack, expecting it to contain Jacobite pamphlets, and the woman fled with it.

A youth climbed onto Darney's back and fastened a horse's bridle over his head. Others tied a long rope around his waist. Beating the drum dolorously as if for an execution, they pushed him into the river. He was so strong that he hardly seemed to gasp at the shock of cold water. "Hell is coming to Yorkshire for men's sins!" he shouted. Several of the men passed over the bridge with one end of the rope. Thus, holding it from both banks, they could balance Darney in the middle of the current at a place where broken pots, animal carcasses and offal had been thrown.

By pulling quickly on the rope they ducked him several times. Wet, bleeding, cold and breathless, Darney continued to prophesy. "Curse us good and proper and we'll release thee!" his tormentors jeered.

The children had found Darney's pack on the river bank and were ransacking its almanacs, bobbins and bits of lace. In imitation of their elders they brought a litter of pups, prodded out their eyes and drowned them at the edge of the river, then laid the dead animals in Darney's hat. The youth who had taken Scotch Will's coat returned with it. It was streaming with different colours — he had been to a dye works and dipped it in the vats. By this time most of the crowd had left and the few who remained were tired of trying to get Scotch Will to curse them. Wet through, muddy, smiling and happy, having relieved their fear of Scotsmen pouring into Hebden Bridge to rape their women, they flung nothing more than taunts at the prophet whilst he climbed onto the other bank. They threw his many-coloured coat down to him from the bridge — they did not want to tempt such a big fellow close, even though he was tired. Darney, without his pack, trailing his coat, climbed up the steep packhorse road to Heptonstall. A small gang of children followed, throwing stones, but they soon gave up or their mothers called them back from the mad preacher.

The wet morning, in which the grey sky and moor seemed to melt and flow together, suddenly broke into a crack of light, blue as the colour of a thrush's egg. It widened and sunshine burst through it like juice out of a pomegranate. The landscape was revealed orange and gold. Patches of gorse were in flower and late roses were still blooming in cottage gardens. Out of reach of his tormentors, Darney sat on a stone, squeezed water out of his coat and put as many clothes as he decently could to dry in the sun. Whilst his things steamed beside him, he lay back, so still that a robin hopped there and sang plaintively. He composed a verse, muttering it aloud in his broad accent but not bothering to write it down.

63

> "At Hebden Bridge the Devil is!
>   And yet I still do pray
> That the good Lord who is not remiss
>   Will visit there some day!"

The robin sang back to him. It seemed so purposeful — its chest swelled, its head held erect — and Darney wondered what that purpose was. When he was rested he put on his partly dried clothes, which now made him shiver with cold, and climbed uphill again, composing another verse aloud.

> "At Hebden Bridge and Heptonstall
>   The work it is begun,
> And Satan's soldiers they do fight
>   For fear we take Blackburn."

There was no-one about. Because of their fear of Scotsmen, people stayed indoors, hiding their pewter and their coins, their silks and silver if they had any, in chimneys and under floorboards, and trying to devise cubby-holes in which to conceal their wives and daughters. Darney expected to be alone until he reached Heptonstall, but at the edge of the town there was a woman waiting for him.

Mary Hepton was a bony woman of the hills, only twenty-five years old but with the tough sinews of an old hen. She was like a stiff yellow stalk of the moorland grass with all its juices sucked out of it, or like a thorn tree growing on thin wind-swept soil. She had stubbornly taught herself to read and write. By persistently questioning clergymen she had forced out of them information that they did not want to give to a woman. At the age of fifteen she realised the special cruelty for women of the doctrine of predestination — their lives were slavery on earth and, stigmatised with Eve's curse, they could not enter man's heaven either. Mary refused to accept it. After a few beatings for her outspokenness, she developed a quiet tough determination. She was brave — too brave, for instance, to think of hiding from Jacobites. To save her family from starvation after a run of bad harvests and snowy winters, she had married a quarryman. Her husband feared her intelligence and so he beat her, on the pretext of her "creeping off" to Darney's meetings. This only made her more fanatical. She bore her punishments knowing that it was the price of her knowledge — which set her apart from Darney's other female disciples who were also wilfully punished at home but who bore it thinking that their lives were miserable because of obscure sins which only their master could, like Christ, forgive.

Darney was able to overbear Mary's sharp intelligence as few men could. He brusquely passed his Bible to her and she carried it. "Why are women like female oxen, Mary? That melancholy look in their eyes and bearing. Both carry in their wombs for nine months. Yon fit woman down Hebden Bridge who follows after me with wash-tubs to stand on — a traitor! She disappeared with my pack and the items of my trade!"

"It is because since Christ's reign men have treated us like dumb oxen. But is that truly the doctrine of Christ? Love thy neighbour . . . . Can man then not love his wife? And not treat her like a beast?"

" 'Give not thy strength to a woman, nor thy ways to that which destroyeth kings.' "

Mary had heard people quoting texts too many times before and she gave up the discussion. She was meeting Darney in the hope of saving him from preaching in Heptonstall where a gang was already prowling around looking for him. "I will preach there although the town has as many devils as there are tiles on its roofs!" Darney answered her angrily, adding "Praise be to God!" with a slow wink.

Heptonstall was similar to Haworth, perched like a grey fortress on a bleak promontory. It was riddled with narrow passageways, flutes in which the wind played. It projected over two deep wooded valleys and the village was surrounded by a narrow fringe of fields above cliffs. The houses were heavy and low to give them stability under the tearing wind and rain. They huddled together as if still protecting themselves from the siege that Heptonstall had suffered during the Civil War. It was a wealthy little town — the money was made in a cloth hall, the "Piece Hall", a main trading centre for twenty miles around — though just now the gold was hidden. Mary Hepton took Darney by back alleys to the house of her wealthy cousin Robert Greenwood at North Gate End, where the preacher could dry himself and be fed before facing another ordeal. She led him in through the kitchen, where he had to stoop his great red head under the beams. The rooms were as bare as the homes of the Dissenters, and you could see the marks where silver plate and the rugs had been removed.

Robert Greenwood, his family and servants had just returned

from morning service. Despite the Jacobites they were in a cheerful mood, because the sun had come out and the sermon had been short. Robert's wool business was prospering and he lived in hope of finding coal in Heptonstall. The maids changing back into their working clothes and the children stiff and frightened of touching anything dirty in their Sunday-best breeches and velvet stared rudely at the amazing visitor. Darney stifled their giggles with his savage glance and a cool wink of his enormous eye. Robert Greenwood, in a hospitable mood but not wishing to offer his hand, waved him towards the fire. Instead the Scotsman, shaking his beard and his uncombed hair that had never been under a wig and that still had bits of twig and river weed clinging to it, roared, "Let us kneel and pray and thank God!" and went down on his knees.

"The man is mad!" Robert exclaimed.

"That is the Lord speaking through him, so that he does not know what he is saying," Mary Hepton explained.

"You believe that?" Mrs Greenwood said, disgusted by the smell of ordure and river that came from him: a smell that she associated with "enthusiasm".

"One who suffers, hopes. And one who hopes, believes," Mary Hepton answered. She was already kneeling, followed by a trembling servant girl. Then the other girl, looking equally terrified, knelt, next Robert and the children. Mrs Greenwood, as if hypnotised, could not stop herself from doing the same. It was as if they had been waiting all their lives for someone to command them to fall to their knees. All muttered "Amens" as Darney thanked God for his deliverance. The pedlar rose, paced up and down restlessly, his head bowed beneath the low ceiling, his squelching boots leaving marks across the floor, his leather creaking. As Robert Greenwood was getting to his feet, Darney bawled again, "Let us pray! Thanks be to God!" Robert at last dared to calm himself by leaning on the mantelpiece. Catching the eyes of the servant girls, he motioned them into the kitchen. This broke the spell. Weighing each of his words, Robert Greenwood said, "There is something in you which I have never seen in any man before." He had expected to be giving Darney a meal with the servants in the kitchen, but instead he offered the pedlar a change of clothes and asked him to dine with the family. The madman did not accept. Instead he told Greenwood to go with Mary Hepton to fetch the people who were waiting for him.

Darney's followers, mostly women, were hiding afraid and cold in

66

a barn, keeping themselves warm with the singing of psalms or hymns and by reciting the Book of Daniel: "When the transgressors are come to the full, a king of fierce countenance, and understanding dark sentences, shall stand up. And his power shall be mighty, but not by his own power: and he shall destroy wonderfully, and shall prosper . . . And through his policy also he shall cause craft to prosper!" They spoke very quietly, terrified of being discovered by the gang that was hunting them. They had confessions prepared and tears were ready to start from their eyes. They were weavers, woolsorters, farmers, domestic servants, masons and other craftsmen. Not the poorest of people, but most of their lives had been awful — you could see it in their eyes, in their scars, their twitches and other gestures, their improvised crutches and starved looks. Although Mary managed to lead them quietly through the town, a small gang still found them and at her cousin's house the shutters had to be drawn. Darney's followers expected their master to prepare them for the Millennium and Mary Hepton, in the twilight and smoke, closed her eyes tight on a vision of it. She saw the earth split in two, as a strong labourer splits an apple in his hands. The mountains tumbled into the cavity with so much dust that the sky was blotted out except for the fierce lightning, but when the earth was settled again it was suffused with a peaceful golden light. When Darney preached she felt that the room was full of angels. . . . Meanwhile angry people were banging on the shutters and doors.

Darney ended all this by creeping out alone through a back way. He was spotted, as he intended, and by this means he led the mob after him and released his congregation. He was rolled in the sewer that ran, thick and slow as soup, down the centre of Town Street. His clothes were torn from him once more and the women cackled at the glimpses of his pale loins and genitals. Limping and half naked, his clothes flung one by one after him, he was chased out of Heptonstall in the direction of Slack. There the crowd gave up. Darney, with a titanic disregard for his suffering, sat down and composed some more doggerel:

> "Haworth's a place that God doth own
> With many a sweet smile;
> With power the Gospel preached therein,
> Which many one doth feel.

Both far and near they hither come,
  Their hungry souls to feed;
And God from Heaven sendeth down
  To them the living Bread.

There's many go rejoicing home,
  In praising of their God,
And want their neighbours for to come,
  And taste the heavenly food.

But whilst the strangers do receive
  The blessing from above,
There's many near the church that starve
  For want of Jesus' love.

They do content themselves, like swine,
  To feed on husks and dirt;
For all their pleasure is to sin,
  And live in carnal sport.''

*

Despite Parson Grimshaw, many Haworth people used the wild moorland weather as an excuse not to travel maybe many miles to church, and it was likely to be a long while before even he got into certain hamlets and farms to reprove them for their absence. There were also old and sick people, and the relatives who cared for them, who were genuinely unable to reach the church. For their benefit Grimshaw had set up regular prayer meetings in distant cottages. He wrote out sermons which were delivered by anyone who was travelling that way and they were read out on Sunday. This system was so successful that Grimshaw's texts penetrated the neighbouring parishes of Todmorden and Halifax. Boundary lines were difficult to keep when they were no more than a peaty gully between a couple of farms, so close together but each separated by miles of bog from its mother church. Many disliked this bursting out of the parish. It sent a shudder through old-fashioned people, as if whatever held their tribe intact was being violated. Yet tradesmen were continuously crossing boundaries. *Trade, trade, everything was for trade, even the church nowadays,* the old people thought. More important for Grimshaw was that other clergymen objected to his piracy of souls and they wanted him expelled from Haworth. They had him brought before Dr Herring, the Archbishop of York.

"How many communicants did you find on coming to Haworth?" the Archbishop asked.

"Twelve, my Lord."

"How many have you now?"

"In winter between three and four hundred, according to the weather. In the summer, nearer twice that number."

Dr Herring was a liberal man with a sense of humour. In any case he was near to retiring and was not interested in the superstitious boundaries of the West Riding any more. He never penetrated into it further than Wakefield, believing it was as far into that barbarous county as "a gentleman could be expected to go". "We can find no fault in Mr Grimshaw, seeing he is instrumental in bringing so many to the Lord's Table," he said.

Unfortunately for Grimshaw, his cottage meetings were soon being "invaded" by every shade of Dissenter. Darney regularly turned up. It was to one of these meetings, at Hardibutts Farm in Crimsworth Dean, that he went after he left Heptonstall. Spies had told Grimshaw that Darney was on his way and that morning he preached against the Methodists — by which he meant all forms of Dissent. Most of the wool-merchants had gone to the trading halls to bring home their cloth and hide it from the Jacobites; nevertheless the church was crowded with the common people, who had less to lose and more to hope for. Nowadays they poured in from other parishes to hear Grimshaw's famous sermons. They filled the churchyard, pushing each other or listening at the door or windows, and the fields around were trampled into a muddy pulp of rubbish and faeces; there was a smell of urine and horses.

There was another special event today. Sally Rushworth, now pregnant by her lover Michael Beever but unmarried, had been ordered by the parson to do public penance and she stood in the aisle before her fellow villagers. She was bare-headed, bare-footed and bare-legged, a white sheet wrapped around her from her shoulders to her toes and she held a white candle. The seven-year-old Jane Grimshaw in the nearest pew saw with horror that Sally was twitching with fear under the sheet. Jane knew Sally well, because Ben Rushworth's daughter was now a maidservant at the house of her father's friend John Greenwood, where Grimshaw had installed her thinking he could thus control this troublesome beauty. But even the clothier's respectable household had not kept Sally from the deserted quarry where the lovers met. Whilst the congregation behind her rose up

69

and down in its prayers, Sally tried not to collapse. After the first lesson she was forced onto a form placed before the pulpit, to face the parson. She tried to hold in her stomach but despite the voluminous humiliating sheet everyone could tell that she was with child. In her broad dialect Sally could hardly pronounce her confession, and her difficulties with "detestable", "indulging", and "unprofitable amusements" were an excruciating humiliation.

"Whereas I good people forgetting my duty t' Almighty God," she whispered after Grimshaw.

"WHEREAS I GOOD PEOPLE FORGETTING MY DUTY TO ALMIGHTY GOD!" he thundered and he made her start again.

"Have committed the detestable sin!"

"Have committed the detestable sin."

"HAVE COMMITTED THE DETESTABLE SIN!"

"Of fornicating and violating and breaking the Sabbath Day."

"Of forcating vilating breakin' th' Sabbath Day . . ." After fifteen minutes of this, Sally was weeping and the convulsions could be seen through the sheet. But she thankfully reached the point of requesting the congregation "to pray with me and for me, saying 'Our Father which art in Heaven . . .' " She did not know whether she knelt or collapsed. The thundering of people falling to their knees behind her sounded like God's judgement itself.

Afterwards Grimshaw preached on Galatians chapter 5 verse 1, "Stand fast therefore in the liberty wherewith God hath made us free and be not entangled again with the yoke of bondage." By "yoke of bondage" he meant Papists, Jacobites and Scotsmen. Grimshaw with the help of John Greenwood and other clothiers was thinking of mustering his own army to drill with hayforks on the moors. £30,000 had been raised by the county's gentlemen at a meeting chaired by Archbishop Herring in York, where tearing up the packhorse routes between Yorkshire and Lancashire had been suggested. . . . John Lockwood and John Greenwood had opposed this motion, which would have hindered trade as well as the rebels. There was already a recruiting sergeant in Haworth and Grimshaw had given him ten pounds of lead, that had been put aside for church roof repairs, to be cast into bullets; and also a list of Papists' houses so that the soldiers could make surprise visits. The sergeant had told him what he now passed on to his congregation — that the Pretender's middle fingers were grown together like the Devil's, that the Rebels' army was made up of the most tattered nasty creatures as had ever been seen and that

Manchester and Carlisle, where they had chained the women and children together in front of the troops who were storming the Castle, were now full of lice. William damned and double-damned his congregation for their faint-heartedness, telling them that a calamity was being prepared by God to bring pagan England to its knees, and that to attend Darney's meetings amounted to treachery against both God and King. He told the poor people, particularly, to enlist and thereby escape their poverty.

Ben Rushworth, brimming with tears and hatred, was heard cackling at the back of the church. Other people sniggered too. The press gang was better even than Grimshaw's sermons at keeping people indoors when they would have liked to be out drinking and singing. Jim O't' Moor Gate, who had been such a carefree man, playing his fiddle and making jokes even at the Haworth Union Society, had enlisted, and they had cut off his bright red hair. Before being taken northwards he was given two days' leave and he did not return, so the soldiers hunted him until he drowned himself in a moorland bog.

Grimshaw dismissed his congregation by roaring out his usual blessing: "Lord tak' all these poor people under thy care and bring 'em in safety to their houses and give 'em their dinners when they get 'ome. But let them not eat a morsel till they have said Grace, because some of 'em are worse than the swine, for even the pigs will grunt over their victuals whilst these say nowt! Then let 'em eat and be satisfied and return thanks to Thee when they've done. Let them kneel down and say their prayers for once at any rate before they go to bed and mebbe Thou'lt preserve them till morning."

"The times we live in are distressing for the common folk," Grimshaw reflected to John Greenwood afterwards. "It is understandable that simple people like Darney and his followers are driven mad by it."

Greenwood laughed and showed all his teeth, white and strong. It was as if he knew that they — unlike his deepest thoughts, which were the devious calculations of a prosperous tradesman — were wholesome and he wanted to show them off. "You should go and speak to them yourself, in your own market language," he said.

In the afternoon Grimshaw set off on his pony to defend his cottage meeting. He had to cross five miles of moorland. Picking his way through the shrivelling heather, he did not look like a clergyman. As the years passed his clothing was becoming more unkempt, in imitation of Christ's poverty, and he wore the bland smile of an optimistic tradesman or weaver. He took his own bread and cheese so as not to embarrass his hosts at Hardibutts Farm.

Once he had cleared the last hamlet he became aware of a figure who had been walking ahead of him and who was now looking over his shoulder nervously. The man suddenly turned off at an angle across the moor. Half an hour later Grimshaw spotted him using a parallel sheep track to reach the same destination as himself. Whenever Grimshaw glanced his way, the man dodged behind a boulder or down into a peat hollow. Grimshaw considered catching him up: he was probably poaching game, or had some idea where coal or minerals might be found. Then Grimshaw thought how to outwit him: he sat for a while on the moortop, where he could see into the only alternative valley which followed a stream that converged with his own path. The man had a distinctive mop of fair hair: it was John Shread. The parson let Shread get well ahead, guessing that he was going to the same destination as himself, Hardibutts Farm.

After an hour's scramble Grimshaw arrived there. It was noticeably tidier than other farms, a mark of Dissenters. It cast bulky shadows from the fading autumn light across a damp slope of Crimsworth Dean. Its only features were a thorn tree and a spring. There was a glitter of water sliding through greener places on the field. Other visitors' ponies, as unkempt as Grimshaw's, were tethered to keep them from the farmer's vegetable patch. Some young men were hiding behind a wall. "Eh up Billy Grimshaw, art expecting the end of the world, too?" they shouted and ducked down, running towards the stream. Apart from these, nobody harrassed the Darneyites here, it being so far from any other hamlet. From the loft of the cow byre attached to the house, there came a rumble of voices. Folk who were more used to shouting across the moors in monosyllables were struggling with the polysyllabic psalms. Grimshaw tethered his pony and entered the lower storey of the byre. In the sudden shot of darkness, all he was aware of at first was the rustled fear of sheep and heifers tethered in the hay.

He climbed a ladder to the loft. William Darney, cleaned up a bit but still in torn clothes, stood facing him from the far end, where he harangued the twenty or so people who sat between, their backs to Grimshaw. There was a potent atmosphere in the twilit room. From time to time they rocked forwards on their knees, rolled about and

72

mumbled their "Amens" loudly. Sometimes they let loose a half-suppressed scream or a private prayer for the Lord to save them from being slaughtered by the Rebels. Whenever anyone stirred, a cloud of dust and chaff rose from the floor. Hardly anyone turned to see Grimshaw. Nobody seemed surprised: those who had only heard him enter assumed that he was another farmer seeking salvation. Grimshaw looked for Shread amongst the congregation, but did not see him.

Darney, placed so that a shaft of light fell upon him through a hole in the roof, was roaring in his Scots accent, "At the greatest extremity of suffering, God always made a way for me to escape! When the sons of wickedness abused my body then my soul was like a watered garden. Praise be to God! My persecutors tumbled me head and ears into a nasty hole full of mire but I was more happy there than they could have been lying on beds of down."

Grimshaw, who had come to claim back his congregation, was moved by this fervour that was so like his own. As the people sang one of Darney's hymns, Grimshaw joined in. The farmers, hearing his familiar great voice, thought that a miracle had occurred. At the end of Darney's service, Grimshaw dramatically gave his blessing to it.

The tenants of Hardibutts Farm, Amos and Mary Lightowler, produced oatmeal biscuits and beer. They were a genteel elderly pair who had drifted down to the status of moor-edgers, one of their few remaining pretensions to gentility being the reading aloud of Grimshaw's sermons. They were nervous at being discovered in Darney's company, indulging in such Dissenting practices as sharing food and drink during the service. But William put them at ease by offering round his own bread and cheese. Darney came towards Grimshaw, smiling, ducking his fierce head below the stone tiles and saying, "When I come into Yorkshire I had no more thought of preaching the Gospel than I had of eating fire. Now see how the Lord has blessed my work! Praise be to God!" As the Darneyites rose from their knees and circulated in the dusty loft, Grimshaw saw what kind of men they were. People with drugged looks pressed upon him and with mad, repulsive intensity asked him what he thought would be the date of the Second Coming.

Darney asked Grimshaw to step outside for a moment. They paced up and down the yard talking very seriously, the pedlar moving with quick jerks, an air of madness about him, his eyes

73

shifting everywhere out of the habit of keeping one step ahead of constables, anti-Jacobites and self-righteous mobs. Grimshaw kept up with him more stolidly, treating the farmyard as if it was his own.

"Mr Grimshaw, you know as well as I do the power of dedicated preaching! And there is a man going around England who is likely to upset the whole world with it and bring it to righteousness. A Mr Wesley. His genius is to organise all his assistants into societies."

"I've heard it said that he is a powerful engine of God who speaks to men in all the common dialects of the Kingdom."

"They say around here that he travels in order to spread the Plague. That he's the Wandering Jew and that he will set fire to cities. I heard him preach once in a street in London. Such a wee frail man! There was a great crowd but he stroked back his hair and fixed his eye on me so that I felt his whole discourse aimed at myself. I dare say that everyone there felt pinned to the cross of his sins by the eye of that man. Then I heard for the first time his wonderful doctrine that I might know my sins forgiven, even whilst I live! He spoke so calmly. God be praised for that day! I think Mr Wesley would be interested in the societies I have founded in Yorkshire. If we were all in harness together we could perfect God's work here also. Could you correspond with him for me?" Darney paused. "Do you like taking tea?" he added. "I know my way around the customs men."

The afternoon was misty, turning dark and starless early. Grimshaw did not dare to stay long but he left spellbound. There were other men, then, travelling the kingdom with the same fervour as himself. Quivering with joy, he could not retire to bed until he had drafted a letter to Mr Wesley. Whilst he wrote, he was distracted. In an uncontrollable wave of self-abasement quite irrational at this moment, but provoked by this unexpected discovery of friends, he longed to be God's slave. Such desires for his Father to come with whips and birch twigs would often overtake him unexpectedly, spoiling his conversation or his ministering of the Host and glazing his eyes. He took from its hiding place the covenant with God that he had composed after Sarah's death and he muttered the words:

"Lord what is my character or desert, that I should desire to be one party in a covenant where Thou, the King of Kings, art the other? I blush even to mention it before Thee — if Thou hold converse with any of Thy creatures, Thy superlatively exalted nature stoops infinitely low. I know that through Jesus, Thou condescendest to visit sinful mortals. To Thee therefore I do now come, laying myself at Thy feet with shame and confusion of face, saying, God be merciful to a sinner, though I am a prodigal son and a back-sliding child!

"And now once more and for ever I solemnly devote all I am and have to Thy pleasure and command. Continue or remove what Thou hast given me, bestow or refuse what I imagine I want, as Thou seest good. I will labour not only to submit, but to acquiesce, not only to bear Thy heaviest afflictions, but to consent to them. Dispose of my affairs, O God, in a manner wholly subservient to Thy glory. And when I have endured Thy will upon earth, call me hence when and in what manner Thou pleasest. . . ."

It grew late into the night. The owls hunted round the Sowdens outbuildings. From his tiny room above the porch, he saw a white barn owl skimming the manure heaps. He heard once, with a fright, Elizabeth wake and overhear his muttering . . . she was no doubt wondering what new madness kept her husband mumbling through the night.

When John Shread saw Grimshaw enter Hardibutts, he had hung about indecisively, not wanting the parson to know that he was now associated with Darney's sect, having left the Union Society. He was a fickle character, born under the sign of Gemini. At one stage he had visited Grimshaw to claim that he wrote poetry. Apparently he had first composed verses for Jonas Appleyard's fiddle, but these had not been written down. Then whilst cutting the grass in the churchyard he realised that he could teach himself to read and write by copying the letters of familiar names on the gravestones and from then onwards, under the influence of books, instead of his rough ballads of bewitchings, ghosts and moorland spirits, he wrote descriptive lines in a regular classical metre. Grimshaw told Shread that he had a remarkable muse for a man born in his humble position upon these rude moors and that he would show his effusions to Elizabeth, who had a more discerning eye for poetry. "Your poet is able to describe a pig but not a Venus. That is because he belongs to the lower classes and is without refinement," Elizabeth had said.

Grimshaw also showed Shread's verses to some local gentlemen including John Greenwood and John Lockwood, thinking that they might get up a subscription for publication. They all agreed that the poet had remarkable inspiration. But they treated this artisan who possessed the Muse's gift as if he had stolen something that rightly belonged to themselves — almost as if he had crept into their houses and stolen the silver. So there was not after all a subscription to publish his verses.

Whilst he hovered outside Hardibutts, Mary Hepton appeared, angry after quarrelling with Darney over the Apocryphal Book of Esdras. Shread was alarmed by her blazing expression, thinking that it was because Grimshaw had denounced the sect.

"Come with me, John, and you may be the first disciple of a new religion," she said. She led him up the moor, the tough sinews of her neck and arms working furiously, whilst occasionally she tugged angrily at her gown when it caught on heather and gorse. Not doubting that he would follow her she led him into a shed where the remains of an old wheat harvest was scattered in dull gold over the floor and was gold dust caught in the cobwebs. She sat upon a bench and he stood before her as indecisive as when he had loitered outside Hardibutts.

She smiled. "Kneel down, John lad, and I will teach thee something." He knelt, his face level with her knees. Her dress, which no matter what size she wore seemed too big for her, was spread like an undrawn curtain before his eyes. Staring a few inches above his head with that disconcerting look of one fixed on an inward vision, she said, "You may be the first that I shall lead into the light, John, if you will obey me. Do not be afraid. Wars and destruction have come because man out of fear of woman has destroyed the goddess who ruled through the ages of silver and of gold. Man's fear makes him fasten a woman's tongue in iron until it runs with blood if she speaks. The Book of Esdras which tells of the strength of woman has been banned out of the Bible. Obey me as men used to in the ten thousand years of silver and of gold and I will show you that woman is Nature, and out of me you will be inspired. Do you not seek inspiration? Then why be afraid? I will teach you contentment to live in harmony with all of Nature that is around you."

She lowered her glance and saw his limbs trembling and his hypnotised look. For a few moments she allowed the strength to flow out of him and into herself, where it would be transformed and returned to him later as inspiration. Pulling her foot out of her shoe she put it like a tongue from under her gown. Shread kissed it, in a smell of sweat and chaff. She lifted her hem. "Go higher," she whispered. Kissing his way up her leg he reached her opening and she slid off the stool on top of him.

Chapter 6

THE GRIMSHAWS FOUND an extra servant to attend to the outdoor work at Sowdens. This was Jonathan Maskew, who had appeared mysteriously in the parish a year before, not telling anyone anything about himself until he met Grimshaw and, in an amazing outpouring, confided everything to him. He was the son of a smallholder in Bingley, only seven miles away. The family had one loom, two cows, six pigs and a dozen hens and geese. Whilst tending these on the common he used to listen to the ranting "hedge preachers" and Dissenters who gathered under the thorn bushes and the oak trees. One afternoon when Jonathan was seventeen some brusque strangers and soldiers drove the cattle, pigs and poultry off the common, straight to the slaughterhouse — for there was now nowhere to graze them — to be sold there at the lowest prices, since they had caused a glut. To take the sting out of this act, employment was provided for everyone in planting the long lines of enclosure hedges that kept them off their own land. Then this work finished also. Jonathan's father, who hitherto had been kind, now turned short-tempered, although Jonathan did everything that he could to please him. The boy did not understand that his father had no alternative but to chase out his eldest son in order to save the whole family from starving. The father excused this cruelty by saying that his son had been sent mad by hedge preachers on the common. He had a dazed "yonderly" look — an absent-mindedness, tripping over things at his feet whilst staring at something in the distance that was invisible to others.

Goodbye mother, goodbye sisters! Whilst Jonathan left home, his father hid in the woods where he had started to poach game. Meanwhile the women made up a bundle of salted pork and whinberry preserve for Jonathan to take with him. After the boy had left his father returned with a couple of stolen woodcock, and wept into his supper. Jonathan did not know where he was going. He headed westwards because they were enclosing fresh land there and he could find more work planting hedges or building walls. He grew so accustomed to sleeping in the fields and barns that after a few months he

78

would have felt uncomfortable in a bed if he had found one. He joined up with other wanderers, who later disbanded when they were persecuted. As a vagabond he was whipped and locked in village stocks. Afterwards he attached himself to fresh groups of "gypsies", who soon broke up again. As he drifted aimlessly working his way across the landscape, he became haunted by the idea that, no matter what he did, God desired his eternal punishment.

Curiously, other dispossessed peasants were drifting as if magnetised towards the valleys of West Yorkshire. In Haworth a kind-hearted farmer found Maskew one morning sleeping with the cattle in his field and the boy stayed to work on the farm. He slept in the barn loft and his clothes and hair became caked with dung. Because of his gloomy expression, children and the other farm servants threw stones at him, while the farmer's wife put about some nonsense that Maskew was half-crazy from an unhappy love affair which had sent him travelling the world. Nobody was sure whether he was Papist or patriot. When Thomas Pighells and other church trustees came around rattling collection boxes for money to fight the Rebels, Maskew gave; but still no-one could quite say whether out of patriotism, or from fear of Pighells. At the end of April 1746, when the gaols of England were full of Rebel sympathisers, the church bells were rung and a great bonfire with an effigy of the Pretender was lit in Haworth for the victory of Culloden, Maskew seemed to celebrate with the others. But then at this time Pighells and his friends broke into the houses of anyone who did not rejoice and raided Papists' homes for clothes with which to dress the Pretender's effigy. So malicious people said that Maskew was a secret Papist who rejoiced only out of fear. Maskew, baited, remained sullen, persecuted by his sense of eternal punishment.

Then he heard Grimshaw preach that one could know one's sins to be forgiven whilst one was still alive, if only one had faith in Christ. This was the first idea that the Haworth people saw stir Maskew to the roots of his being. But what did "faith in Christ" mean? What did one have to do, he asked Parson Grimshaw? The upshot was that Jonathan moved to Sowdens where he was found work as general servant, devotedly attending to the parson's horse, his two cows and his poultry. He slept in the barn loft — Elizabeth wouldn't have him in the house — where the ten-year-old John Grimshaw used to spy on him. Creeping close one day, John saw that Maskew had set up a broken piece of mirror before the hatch through which hay was heaved into the loft, and was posturing in front of it in the manner of a preacher. As the pigeons flew in and out Maskew addressed them as his "congregation". He ordered them to kneel and pray for forgiveness of their sins. "Croo! croo! croo!" went the pigeons, bobbing their necks stupidly before they flew away. Another time, Maskew was found conducting a mock funeral service for Grimshaw's enemies, Benjamin Rushworth and Thomas Pighells.

One dusk when Maskew and Grimshaw were returning over the moors, the parson casually picked up a pair of ram's horns (quite a few were to be found there, from sheep that had died during the winter), held them against his ears and began to smirk as he danced around clumsily in the bog. It was a frightening experience for Maskew, who always, but particularly at dusk, sensed demons on the moortops, where he continually resisted the temptation to turn round upon the creatures of his imagination that stalked him. Now it seemed as if Parson Grimshaw had changed into one of these monsters, dancing, lifting his feet heavily out of the squelchy black peat and rushes before him.

Grimshaw put the horns under his coat and said nothing about his mischievous performance until they were back at Sowdens. Then he asked Elizabeth to stitch him a mask out of black velvet. Delighted to have some amusement returning to her life, she worked at it through the following day, contriving also a couple of wicked-looking ears as hairy as a pig's. She suggested a tail made out of rope, and she frayed the end and waxed it into a barbed point. That evening it was fixed to Grimshaw's belt, the end looped over his wrist and under his gown. Maskew, also dressed in black, carried the rest of the Devil's disguise.

When people were coming out of the inn Grimshaw and Maskew took up a position in a narrow passageway between it and Michael Beever's house. They were growing stiff and cold and Maskew was wanting to give up, when Michael came singing home. He stopped to pee against a wall, proud of the fine and virile arc he could make, lifting it as high as possible, concentrating, watching the splendid cloud of vapour. Whilst Michael's back was turned William adjusted his false ears, spread his arms and arranged the end of the tail visibly over his wrist. Maskew grimaced behind him.

At last the young man turned round. Grimshaw stepped into the middle of the path. "Whoo! whoo! whoo!" he went, like an owl. Michael's heart leapt, his stomach became cavernous. In one moment of such vividness that he peed himself, he regretted all his sins and longed, oh how he longed, for an opportunity to make better use of his life in future. For a second he hoped that maybe what he saw was an apparition — a queerly-shaped bush, a trick of the light. But no: "Whoo! whoo! whoo!" the Devil repeated, and then boomed out in a voice that Michael, if he'd had his wits about him, would have recognised, "Michael Beever! Michael Beever! I've come to claim you for my own! Thou'rt a man cast for evil deeds! Let me take you to the land of the dead where you can be wicked for ever, to remain in torment for your sins through all eternity!"

Michael's knees gave way, and he fell onto the stones. He prayed and took his last gasping look at this world — the beauty of the beads of mist on the walls and bending the rank yellow grass; his own liquids, glittering with rainbows there. He saw Hell opening before him — a blackness that swept over his eyes, so that for several dizzy seconds he could see nothing whatsoever. Then it cleared for a moment, he saw the Haworth walls again, and the Devil standing over him, wearing a priest's black gown and speaking in a Lancashire accent.

The demon rubbed its hands together. "Thou knowst how to treat the lasses, Michael Beever! Get what you can and never marry the girl!" Then Grimshaw heard someone coming and he hurried his speech. "Never marry Sally Rushworth and you'll be sure t'end in my clutches at finish!" he chuckled, and vanished, quickly, as the Devil might be expected to vanish. Michael's friends later found him clamped face-down to the damp stone passageway, shivering and crying. Sally Rushworth became Sally Beever very soon after.

Apart from a few events of this kind, the parson's wife disliked her husband's activities and his new circle of friends. They embodied all that Elizabeth Grimshaw found mean and inelegant about her dismal Haworth environment. Whilst William more and more rambled the moors with Maskew and whilst John Grimshaw ran wild about the farm, Elizabeth (like Sarah after her marriage) took to her couch imagining that she was sick; doing nothing very demanding and yet sincerely believing that her sewing taxed her strength. William's enthusiasm left no alternative for his wives — he seemed to need them lying there, so as not to interfere with his own freedom. Like Sarah, Elizabeth had not been taught to read or write, so she could not fill her time by sending letters. Oh, how she longed for a child of her own, a daughter whom she might dress in ribbons and silks! All her fine ambitions were in ruins. She had dreamed of living in a hall, of purchasing from Liverpool or Bristol a negro boy to wait on her, a silver collar with her name on it around his neck. She had imagined that the life of a clergyman's wife would be like that of her sister Mary (married to William's brother John) who was a queen in local society. Instead, Elizabeth was immured in a moorland farm-house with a bleak evangelist who was too mean to have coal fires lit on any but the coldest days, with the cattle and other beasts moaning and trampling the fields outside her window, and her only attendant, apart from Molly, the half-witted servant-boy Maskew. Her efforts at refinement were reduced to a futile attempt to confine Molly to her kitchen. When the parson was at home the girl *would* come creeping back to the withdrawing room . . . After a great effort Elizabeth succeeded and Molly was taught her place. Mistress and maid were thus banished to their separate lonelinesses of kitchen and parlour, so Elizabeth no longer heard the moorland girl's chatter and songs.

Then sickness did visit Elizabeth as she apparently desired. In October 1746 Haworth suffered one of its regular epidemics of typhoid fever. Elizabeth's first symptoms, a general malaise, fatigue and aching bones, loss of appetite and headaches, were hardly noticeable in her case. Even when she was delirious William still slept peacefully by her side at night and was absent for much of the day. The only hint that Elizabeth might be sick came when Molly, larding the children's bodies with goose fat and stitching their clothes up for the winter (a vulgar practice that Elizabeth detested) told them that it would protect them from "the Plague".

"We are lucky to have good Mr Grimshaw to pray for us," John Greenwood said to Elizabeth. "And I have someone in my family, with my son Paul following your husband as if he was his own father. I can't think how we managed to keep free of the Devil's teeth in the days before we had these to pray for us. My lad tells me that the world looks and smells differently since he first heard your husband. That I don't understand too well. Money smells of money and a full-ing mill smells like a fulling mill whether you are Christian, Jew or Methodist." Such wry comments, leaving you unclear as to the speaker's true opinion, were typical of the clothiers; Elizabeth had heard this kind of talk from established men all her life and it made her feel secure; so she trusted her husband's friend. "I hear that William goes to Luddenden a great deal. What does he do there?" she asked. Elizabeth's wary knowledge of what was actually happening outside Sowdens startled John Greenwood somewhat. "He just sits there, 'appen thinking about past times," he answered. On William's next return from evangelising Elizabeth, with her staring eyes fixed on an invisible object as if she was sleepwalking, quietly said these words that leached onto his memory: "It's easy to stay in love with your past loves, my husband, it's like loving animals. Sarah can't answer you back." Whereupon William fetched the apothecary for her madness.

Appleyard was busy and harassed, for there was no better time than this to obtain bodies for research. He left Ruth Appleyard to tend the sick and she nursed them from the resources of that extraordinary tenderness of hers which had in the first place led her to "marry" her brother when he seemed so much in need of her. Now she calmed the sick with a smile, although her heart was wrenched by their condition. She prescribed for them as well as she could, expressing her opinion with such dignity that people had faith in her. Meanwhile Jonas bribed the workhouse keepers, or paid for rumours that led him to haunt moorland graveyards after thunderstorms, half the time on fools' errands. Sometimes he missed the only day in a season suitable for harvesting oats from his two tiny enclosures in order to visit some shallow grave that had spilled its contents after a storm. Though no quack but a member of the Society of Apothecaries, he laid great store by bleeding and was often criticised for taking too much blood and for carelessly spilling it on floors.

Elizabeth's stomach had swollen, in mockery of that pregnancy for which she had longed, and the apothecary tried to deflate it with leeches that he dragged out of a sinister-looking jar. Afterwards he applied a hot flannel dipped in stewed camomile and poppy capsules. For her headaches in the evenings, he cut off her hair and cooled her temples with a herbal mixture followed by a spirit wash, dabbing at her forehead with the same expert gestures with which he played the fiddle. To sweat the illness out of her, she had to sit up to her knees in hot water in which was dissolved two ounces of mustard and afterwards her legs were rubbed with hot towels. Half the time she was delirious, shivering petulantly in the draughts.

Jane spent much of her time indoors with her stepmother, bringing

83

her endless drinks of water. The child, nauseated by the smells of congealed sweat and diarrhoea, watched as Elizabeth flushed, her eyes swelled and became moist. After an hour opposite symptoms would appear; she went white and cold and the eyes that had sparkled feverishly became dull. In another hour the flushes and fever returned. In her delirium Elizabeth raised her trembling hand and snatched at invisible objects, screaming out, "What's that to you? Be gone, be gone!" Her tongue was dry and brown and she hung it out of the side of her mouth.

Jane understood that her stepmother was dying. The child at nine years of age was accustomed to death. Although she could not remember her mother's passing, yet she had a deeply embedded impression, given once in a dream, of her mother smiling blissfully, with transparent wings and a long white dress, on her way to Heaven. Jane had watched her Aunt Mary die in 1743; a long agony which the child believed was her being dragged stage by stage down into Hell because she was a witch, eventually to be pitched into everlasting fire. Jane had often overheard her father complaining about Elizabeth's lack of faith. Where, then, was her stepmother to go?

After William's correspondence with the Wesleys, Charles paid a visit to Haworth and was shown around by Grimshaw, Paul Greenwood (hampered as always with a book under his arm), Maskew, Jane and her brother John — whose wild dashings around the fields and the middens horrified Charles Wesley who believed that children were corrupted by "play". The town was almost empty, echoing with the "tap, tap," of the mason chipping at gravestones, and the church bell tolled all day for the dead. People had gone mad with delirium this week. A dying woman had torn out a bailiff's stomach with a kitchen knife, and a man who shouted for the Devil to fetch him at once had to be chained up. A few took the town's afflictions philosophically; one man, for instance, had his gravestone carved early, before mortality overtook the mason, and had it placed facedownwards for a doorstep until his hour came to meet his Maker.

As Wesley's party came by, a few sad silent people gathered with their buckets at Head Well. Sickly damp yellow leaves massed in gutters and against walls because no-one had the heart to sweep them away. Charcoal fires glowed behind the oiled-paper windows of the woolcombers' shops, but nobody could be heard laughing or talking there. All over town, there was only wailing, and uncomprehending

84

stares for the stranger. They suspected that Wesley was a government spy. Haworth was as if besieged — at the bottom of the hill was a stone pillar with a hollow scooped out of the top and filled with vinegar, and into this money was placed for goods left by tradesmen who would not enter the "plague town". And if anyone from Haworth was recognised in another village, they stoned him.

What most struck Wesley about Haworth was not its sickness, for he had seen that in many places, but the water that ran everywhere, over the walls and through the doors without people taking the slightest notice of it. Whilst he was thinking over a text for the sermon that he was going to preach the following day, on Isaiah chapter 35 — "The wilderness and the solitary places shall be glad for them; and the desert shall rejoice and blossom as the rose" — a woman darted out and grabbed Grimshaw's arm. She was Benjamin Rushworth's wife Mercy, who begged the parson to come to her daughter Sally, so they went with her to Rushworth's house. It was in a block of cottages piled above and against one another at all sorts of levels to fit in with the steep hillside. The upstairs room, though at the front it had a view over the valleys, at the back had the cellar of another cottage so that the wall trickled with seepage. A sewer ran under the floor and the smells rose between the seams of the flagstones. Sally with her year-old baby, her mother and grandmother — who were indoors most often — felt continually depressed, yet were so used to the smells that they did not recognise them as the cause of their vertigo and nausea. Fresh water had to be fetched in a half-mile walk from near the graveyard, so naturally they saved this for drinking and used inferior water for cooking and washing. Doubtless Sally would not have caught the fever if she had stayed a maidservant at the Greenwoods'. But after Michael Beever had unexpectedly married her they had set up home in her parents' house, where they made their living out of one loom and a spinning wheel. Michael Beever was destroyed by his calamity and could do nothing but quake and cry in a chair.

The grandmother was ready to kiss the parson's hand for his visit. Grimshaw, irritated, pulled away from her and the old woman looked quite upset, unable to understand how much he detested "idolatry". The baby, who had been nicknamed "Little Ben Rushworth" before Michael Beever assumed some of his responsibilities, threshed about restlessly in the grandmother's arms. William looked at it distastefully. "Nature is so polluted with evil that God would be just to pack any infant straight from the womb off to Hell,'' he said. Little Ben Rushworth obliviously blew delicate transparent bubbles at the harsh world into which he'd been born, while Grimshaw impatiently led his party clattering over the stone floors into the rear room, bawling out, ''The hand of God is upon you and the Devil is ready to take you and Hell to swallow you up — and now look it's send for Grimshaw as fast as thee can!'' Ben Rushworth, sitting glumly, caught Grimshaw's eye, held his glance but said nothing.

Sally was delirious. Her beautiful hair was matted with sweat. She smelled horribly, like all typhoid victims. In only a week's time she had lost her plumpness and her dry yellow skin hung in ugly folds. No treatment had been given to her, other than her grandmother's herbal syrups, because the apothecary could not spare leeches and medicines for such ne'er-do-wells as the Rushworths. Mercy Rushworth held Sally's hand which was trembling violently, while the grandmother struggled to quieten the baby so that the preachers could do their work. Paul Greenwood stood uncomfortably as if wishing to hide himself behind the door, coughing politely, fumbling with his Bible and looking for a quotable text. Maskew stood at the foot of the bed, Wesley went to one side of it and Grimshaw to the other. In his usual fashion Grimshaw shouted as if he intended to wake the dead: ''I've managed to stable three-quarters of the heathen dead of this parish in the Kingdom of God, but this time you've Mr Wesley to save your souls! All you need do is repent! Has tha an idea of what the eternal torments of Hell are that await you?''

Sally writhed, delirious, tortured by the pain of urine dammed up in her kidneys and hardly able to hear the preachers who began to outdo one another in their depictions of Hell. Whilst the old woman tried to clean up the bed and Mercy Rushworth steadied the trembling of the girl's hands, Maskew told her that she was experiencing only one fraction of the pain that awaited her for all Eternity. Paul Greenwood said that Hell was a place of red hot ashes, but Grimshaw and Wesley told Sally that it burnt with flames leaping to the height of a man.

There was a look of terror on Sally's face. Ben Rushworth stared at the floor, ready to be sick with fear, and Mercy was hiding her weeping. Whilst Mr Wesley calmly gave final absolution to Sally, Jane looked around the room at the crude wooden furniture, the wooden bowls and spoons and the chaff leaking out of Sally's

86

pillow. On the table was a box which had three separate locks. It held the subscriptions to the Union's Burial Club — even the children saved up a penny a week towards the expenses of their own funerals. The keys were distributed to different officers of the Union Society and all three of them had to be present to open it. As the party left, Grimshaw asked Ben Rushworth to donate Sally's clothes for distribution to the poor. Ben gathered shoes, cotton petticoats and aprons, bundled them together (for his wife was incapable of doing anything) and thrust them, still without saying a word to his visitors, at Grimshaw.

The evangelists crossed the yellowing fields back to Sowdens.

"It has been amazing to witness what weeping, roaring and agonies many people have been seized with because of their sinful state and the wrath of God!" Grimshaw shouted.

Wesley was moved by the sheer power of Grimshaw's ministry in this barbarous place. "Haworth has become the Lord's pew," he murmured.

"I preach down man and preach up Christ in language that those hereabouts understand," Grimshaw answered.

Although Grimshaw was tired and perhaps sickening himself, as soon as he reached Sowdens he led them all into his wife's room. Elizabeth was a horrible sight. Her swollen tongue was now black and lolled out of her mouth, trembling and jerking in spasms. Delirious, she could not tell whether there were two, six or ten visitors in her room; she saw only vague shadows. She coughed as if she, like Sarah, had consumption and she spat blood. She tried to cry out for water. Her appeal began as a howl, whilst she stared at something that terrified her hanging invisibly about three feet away. Her voice then sank to a gurgling noise from the back of her mouth. Only Molly understood it, for she had been pouring water down her mistress's unquenchable throat all afternoon.

Grimshaw sent Maskew to bring some leather straps from the stable. During his absence, they prayed — a hum so regular that it seemed menacing, like an invasion of hornets. Maskew returned with a rattle of straps and buckles. Elizabeth groaned, moaned. Grimshaw, concerned entirely for Elizabeth's spiritual fate, bound her arms to her sides and her body to the bed, controlling her convulsions whilst he talked to her as she tottered on the brink of Heaven or Hell. She tossed her head this way and that, her eyes flaring as she

87

struggled to say something with her swollen tongue. With an effort they caught it: a familiar text from Corinthians: "Though I bestow all my goods to feed the poor — and though I give my body to be burned — and have not charity — it profiteth me nothing." Her desperate effort to warn her husband was lost in violent spasms. Molly, who best grasped her mistress's words, grew pale whilst she interpreted Elizabeth's terrible final stuttering, in panic before her eternal burning, cravenly accepting salvation at last and begging God's forgiveness.

Chapter 7

ELIZABETH'S BURIAL AT Heptonstall that November was what the Methodists called "a grand little occasion". There had been a "revival" of religion in Heptonstall, as had happened in Haworth shortly after Grimshaw went there. It began with the conversion of Robert Greenwood after Darney's visit a year ago. Fire was the metaphor in the mind of every Methodist at Elizabeth's graveside. Religion had quickened, consumed, spread from house to house, flared, burnt from the housetops, swallowed men, women and children in the fires of God's wrath so that they could not settle to their work before they had knelt, prayed, and been forgiven for their sins — it was said that you could hear the cries rising to God with the smoke out of the chimney pots. Their persecutors had "melted like tallow in a bonfire", they said. Women gossiping around their hearths heard the wailing next door, grew silent and then they too began howling. So the fever of conversion spread from street to street, amongst weavers at their looms, amongst woolcombers and farmers. Robert Greenwood's miners, who were driving tunnels into the hillside but never finding coal, grew morosely conscious of their unhappy condition and of their sins. Some were converted through thinking that if the Greenwoods were, it must be good for trade. They stopped work and prayed until their knees were sore. "I'm smothered in 'ell's fires! Save me!" they cried. The already-saved shouted on the others. "Keep praying lad, dunna give up! Tread the old Devil underfoot! Thou'lt know the descent o'mercy when it comes! What *peace* it is, lads!" "I can't! I can't!" "Struggle on lad, struggle on. Thou'lt win in the end!" And then at last there came an orgasmic easing into bliss. "I'm saved!" Many a man and woman rolled over as if drunk.

A few left the town because they could not bear this shouting and crying. Mary Hepton's husband stubbornly drank until one night he died of a heart attack. Robert Greenwood turned a large part of his house into a preaching room and other offices for the Darneyites, who had now become Methodists. There was a special kitchen for them and a bedroom for visiting preachers. William Darney, nearly forty years of age, suffering the first pangs of arthritis from standing out-of-doors and being thrown into manure heaps and rivers, was overjoyed to see the first of his groups acquire property and become relatively respectable Methodists. Yet he kept a lingering regret for the wilder and more passionate days when he had dreamt of the Millennium, and often came to poke the fires burning in Heptonstall. William Shent, a preacher from Leeds who was also a barber, apothecary and dentist, came there too. Also John Nelson, a stonemason who had been conscripted into the army because of his preaching and sent northwards to the Scottish border — but when he turned it into a preaching campaign, being made safe from hostile crowds because he was wearing the King's uniform, the authorities released him.

The fires of conversion had died down during the last year and Elizabeth's funeral was a chance to revive them. Darney's local society from Bacup, together with members of Nelson's and Shent's parties from other towns, filled the church. Bands of Methodists were now beginning to travel about the moors to attend preachings. Darney, Nelson, Shent, Mary Hepton, William's friend John Greenwood and his son Paul, William Grimshaw, John, Jane, their grandfather John Lockwood and Molly Shackleton were there; William's brother John and his wife Mary (who still enjoyed the lugubrious atmosphere of funerals), and several of Elizabeth's family. All these gathered around the grave dug in the nave of the church. The non-Methodists stood out, their dress looking stylish, even coquettish by comparison. They were noticeably aloof from the artisan Methodists — the stonemason, the cobbler, the maidservant, and the barber William Shent who that morning had given everyone at Sowdens a shave and a haircut, and yesterday for small fees had pulled several teeth in Haworth.

"And do you still think that your encouraging the lower orders to be Methodistical is good for them or for the stability of society, William?" Mary Grimshaw asked, aware of both the Methodists inside the church and their persecutors, intimidated by the presence of the gentry, who prowled with sticks and stones outside.

"To seek salvation is good for all of us," Grimshaw answered.

"You know the lower classes better than I do, you spend so much time with them. But it seems to me fortunate that we've already hidden the church plate."

"The Lord will have his way."

"*With the church silver!* My poor sister suffered terribly from enthusiasm." Mary began to cry. She became a bundle of black shining silk, like a rook huddled in a rainy wind. William Shent's ten-year-old son John stared at her: he had heard so much about death, God, and being "prepared". His father had tried to get him to say "God" as the first word that he spoke — "go go go!" he said when other babies said "da da da". The child had been brought here especially to witness an instructive funeral and the father marked how his son stared into the earth-smelling hole as the coffin grated onto its bed of water and small stones under the nave. In the yard the protesters were arguing that the Yorkshire they had always known was being turned upside down by madmen. William went out and preached a sermon on how Elizabeth, who had also been for so long a "great opposer", had on her death bed been convinced of her sin and "redeemed".

A funeral feast was held at the Cockcrofts' house at Mayroyd, Hebden Bridge. There John Greenwood and John Lockwood discussed with Grimshaw the problems they were having with the wool-combers. The Haworth Union Society was demanding a minimum piece-rate for combing and if the master refused to pay it, he could not find anyone to do the work. The combers did not want anyone to employ a non-unionist. The master clothiers had hired spies who told them that the Union was connected with similar ones in Keighley, Bradford and Halifax, thus preventing the clothiers from taking their work to be done elsewhere. In these towns the unions could also stop the masters from prosecuting their work-people for bad workmanship. Several "mobs" had attacked fulling mills and clothiers' establishments. And who was the woolcombers' spokesman? Ben Rushworth.

John Lockwood came out with a plan to rid both the West Riding wool-men and also the Haworth parson of a great nuisance. A few days later Ben Rushworth was arrested and charged with having stolen cloth from tenter frames. Two soldiers marched him in irons to Bradford. They carried rolls of cloth — well over five shillings' worth, which made the "theft" a capital offence — and which the staring people of Haworth were expected to believe had been found in Ben's house. They remembered him as an honest man. Ben knew this and kept his head up amongst them, although his legs were giving way. But at Bradford he discovered that the most powerful

men in the district had charged him with atheism, sedition and coining as well as with stealing wool. With a feeling as if a bottomless
chasm had opened up in his stomach, Ben realised that he was
doomed. The men around the magistrate watched him turn white.
They thought that Ben knew his guilt had been discovered. Ben,
struggling to recover, hardly heard anything else that was said to
him. He had awakened into a new world, the one of those who are
about to die. There everything was intensely vivid and things that
had before seemed important, now fell in an instant away. It was like
a religious conversion.

Ben was kept in the Bradford gaol for the night. It consisted
of two cages, one each for men and women, beneath the slaughterhouse in Ivygate. Blood dripped into the cells. During the day the
prisoners heard the squealing and bawling of pigs and cattle being
slaughtered, and at night their frightened moans. The damp brought
on Ben's bronchial cough. His cell-mate preached the coming
of the Apocalypse: he was crazy from many previous imprisonments
when apothecaries had tested new drugs on him. An idiot woman
was in the next cell. Only her hands were visible, grasping through
the bars as she encouraged the ravings of the crazy preacher. A
crowd outside threw slaughterhouse offal and baited Ben as if he
were a Methodist — to the weavers, his "crime" of stealing cloth
was worse than atheism, radicalism or murder, because it struck
at their livelihood. Ben struggled to appear unafraid. Other men
before him had gone through this and he had often asked himself
whether he could survive such a test. Like those others, he now had
only his immortality to think about and he was determined not to
ruin it.

Mercy Rushworth had followed him but it was night-time before
she could get close to give him bread, water and a candle. At sight of
these good things, Ben's eyes dampened. " 'Who can find a virtuous
woman?' " he quoted to her from the Book of Proverbs. " 'For her
price is far above rubies. The heart of her husband does safely trust
in her. She seeketh wool, and flax, and worketh willingly with her
hands. She is like the merchants' ships; she bringeth her food from
afar.' " Mercy began to cry and Ben comforted her by talking softly
of the beauty of the slaughterhouse yard, where a moon turned to
dark purple the pools of blood and water. He pointed out the stars.
"Some say they're but great lumps of dead substance, but what I see
are trembling lights as delicate as spring flowers. Now what is the

truth?'' Mercy began to fumble with her dress, and Ben remembered how in their house whenever he spoke of politics she would nervously make herself busy with household tasks, spinning or making oatcakes — how far away already was that household scene!

"The parson will help us," Mary said.

"I don't think so."

"He helps everybody. He is moved by love for mankind."

"But not for the like of us."

Before dawn Ben was marched to Leeds and the day after to York Castle, in a party that gathered more prisoners from village gaols on the way. Many of them were Methodists who were being conscripted into the army. The damp winter dawn rose upon a flat landscape, with brick houses, huge beech and elm trees, a slow broad river and newly-planted quickthorn hedges. Ben's legs were used to hills and they felt strange upon the flat land. At Leeds the prisoners were put on show in the street, mainly so that the Methodists could be baited whilst they worked themselves up trying to convert the crowd. A woman shoved her face close to a manacled preacher and shouted, "Now where's thy God? Thou saidst tha was no more afraid of his promise failing than tha was of dropping through th'eart of the earth!" To which the Methodist replied, sharp as a ferret, "Seventh chapter of Micah, 'Rejoice not against me, O mine enemy: when I fall, I shall arise; when I sit in darkness, the Lord shall be a light unto me . . . Then she that is mine enemy shall see it.' " Ben was very moved by the dignity and the bravery of the Methodists.

Mercy Rushworth trailed from the Pighells to the Greenwoods to the Lockwoods in begging for Ben's defence. She often had to carry Sally's baby with her over the moors. It was late November and fogs lingered threatening to spread over the boglands. It took Mercy all her courage to push open the heavy gates, walk through the ornamental gardens where she thought gardeners were sneering at her and to knock on grand doorways, hearing the huge dogs leaping up on the other side. Ben calmly told her that these visits would be useless. Mercy could not understand the acceptance that had come over her husband since his arrest but she loved him deeply for his philosophy and bravery. She herself refused to feel reconciled and hopeless. When she saw Lockwood looking so solid and fatherly, with a smile that wrinkled the corners of his eyes, she trusted him. She read a great sadness in his face — his two daughters and his son dead. He kindly enquired the baby's name.

"They call him Little Ben Rushworth."

"After the grandfather? There will soon be no . . ." He was going to say "confusion". "Where is the father?"

"He's gone to be a soldier. There's no work as weavers for the like of us."

"The King must have soldiers for our foreign wars."

" 'Appen so."

"What do you think of my improvements?" By building a new front on one side of the building, Lockwood was turning its face away from the woods in which it had snuggled for centuries, either for shelter or for shame; and with big windows and a classical front it would now look proudly and securely over the Calder Valley from which the best of cattle, game, honey, fish and pieces of wool were brought to Ewood. Lockwood's yeomen ancestors had waited for generations, like pike with their teeth bared hidden in reeds at the edge of a river, for the chances of land and property to drift towards them and then — as if hardly believing that the earth could be theirs — to enclose it in stone walls, just as they enclosed their family with circumspect marriages. John Lockwood wanted a worthwhile legacy for his only grandson, John Grimshaw. "Is it as fashionable as I've been told it is, to overlook a picturesque view? I would rather keep watch on my servants in the yard."

"With all the improvements one man does the work of ten and gets no more for it. There's nowt for folk to do but pine to death," Mercy said, and suddenly found herself talking like her doomed husband. She looked through the window and saw carts loaded with human bones and coarse grey powder, a fertiliser for Lockwood's enclosures and garden. Mercy had witnessed plenty of sickness in her life, but looking at bones and broken skulls — or perhaps it was because she had reached the limit of her sadness and disgust — Mercy vomited. Before a revolted John Lockwood she was hustled into the yard, protesting that she'd had no chance to discuss her errand.

To save her husband she crossed the moor on Sunday, even though she had been brought up piously and had kept to it. As she walked through Haworth where everyone else was going in an opposite direction to church, she felt cast out of a tribe, or like a dog without a master — an uncanny loneliness which she realised must

94

also have often been her husband's emotion. After she had walked so uncomfortably the twenty miles to Ewood, she was sent to the back entrance. The yard was as noisy as a market with weavers bringing in their pieces. There was a smell of freshly-dyed cloth. Bales were packed for shipping. Mercy was kept waiting for an hour, shifting from foot to foot, looking up at the strange carvings peeping out of the walls. John Lockwood was a shade less hospitable this time. Because of bad weather and the raids by French and Dutch pirates, there were no ships sailing to Holland. It looked as though there would be no trade from Yorkshire until the spring. She should have his problems, he told her. How much happier it was to be a simple shepherd tending one's flock in the hills. . . . The third time, John Lockwood had gone to Norwich to buy wool and she was met by servants who had acquired their master's cold unscrupulousness.

It was the same at the other houses. John Greenwood invited her into his homely parlour. He stretched his legs before the fire and smoked his pipe. He spoke slowly and deliberately as if she was a child, remembering that her daughter had worked in his house. But as soon as he began to offer some hope, he cut it short with his peculiar loud laugh, spat tobacco juice into the fire and started on a different subject: the apprentice who had woven a piece that Ben was supposed to have stolen was not to be found. Mercy might wait. She waited all afternoon feeling more and more in everyone's way and still the apprentice did not show up. At last Mercy walked home, hungry, in the dark and unsatisfied. She realised that to have dealings with the master clothiers was like entering a sticky cobweb that they wove to catch such flies as herself, letting her struggle haplessly until she had no strength left.

One day Ben, lost in his thoughts, was suddenly dragged, blinking, fastened in irons, up into the brilliant light of the courtroom. His legs were fixed two feet apart with an iron contraption called the "shears". Riveted around his waist was an iron girdle and on two short chains from that were wrist manacles. His irons clanked in the murmurous quiet. As he glared with fear like a trapped animal, he saw Mercy and his mother sitting nearby and some lawyers fanning themselves to drive away his smell. The judge, like Charles Wesley in Haworth, clutched a prophylactic bunch of flowers. Ben saw his own Bible, with his annotations in it, lying on a table.

95

"You are a believer in reform but you say that you are also loyal to the church?" the judge began.

"Jesus Christ was a reformer!" Ben answered angrily, his eyes flaring with a mixture of fear and courage, his throat dry from not speaking during his imprisonment, and the spittle flying from his lips.

"Much good it did him! He was executed!" the judge chuckled. Laughs flew around the courtroom. Mercy Rushworth hid her tears.

"Many people attend divine service in your parish?" the judge asked Grimshaw.

"They are on their way to Hell with their eyes open at least," the parson answered, his lips pouting in the stuffy room.

"And is the criminal before us one of their number?"

"He does not attend divine service. Moreover his arguments tend towards a denial of God."

"When my child was lost on the moors and found two months later wi' his head gnawed to the skull by dogs, the first person told was Jonas Appleyard the apothecary who wanted the body for dissection! He gave me five shillings for my own son!" This outburst of Ben's was added to other evidence of his seditious opinions.

"He did not join in celebrations for the downfall of the Rebels at Culloden," Grimshaw added.

The Greenwoods' and the Lockwoods' servants said that they had heard Ben deny God and curse the King. An apprentice swore he had woven the cloth discovered in the Rushworths' cottage. Soldiers claimed that they had found the implements of coining — the scissors used to clip the gold from the edges of coins, the pans for melting it down, and the die for stamping out fake money — when they tore up Rushworth's floorboards.

A few days later Ben was taken for his execution at the Tyburn, in an open cart that was long and narrow like a coffin. His face down to the root of his neck turned white. Around him was a fence of pikes held by the soldiers. Unable to look into the crowd who shouted and laughed — or worse, stared with absorbed currant-like expressionless eyes — Ben turned to the grey pre-Christmas sky, clasping his hands together to stop their trembling, so people thought that he was praying. Mercy Rushworth, walking behind and dreading mostly that her husband might collapse, clutched his last letter:

I feel no fear in passing through the shadow of death into eternity.

It is as if I merely went into another room. So I hope you will think we will meet together in Heaven. My beloved, this is what I have to send to you. My Plato, my Bunyan and my Bible. Keep them and teach my grandson to read and gain understanding. One pair of stockings and a shirt. God bless you. Your Ben for all eternity.

The grandmother held the baby, and members of the Friendly Society were there to comfort them whilst the crowd jeered.

Ben's gallows stood on a slight rise in the ground at the edge of York. They tied his hands to prevent his tearing at the noose. The thought of the rope — as if his mind had been on anything else! — deepened his panic at the coming pain. He was afraid, all right. What must he go through as his face turned blue and bloated? They were shouting for him to confess, but he felt his throat dry, as if full of stones. He tried to daze himself — to have no thoughts, but to live for this moment which, at least, could not be taken from him. It was worth trying not to show fear. All those out there lived in a different country — faces strange to him, every one of them. He dared not search out Mercy. There was Bill O't'Cows. His look, which was almost expressionless, fortified Ben — he could read Bill's thoughts: "Stand up to 'em, lad!" Over the heads Ben saw a plain, fading into fog, where gangs of men were planting enclosure hedges to keep them off their own common land. Thinking of this, Ben tried to speak, not of Sabbath-breaking as the crowd hoped, but of political philosophy. They began to throw rubbish and stones and the hangman hurried to put the rope around Ben's neck. Ben knew that, for his own kind, the words that he uttered at his execution would be the only ones to be taken down and remembered. In a panic, struggling with his feet to grasp at the cart that was drawing away from him, Ben screamed out, "If your God makes the misery I see about me then I want nowt to do with him!"

William Shent had brought his son John to watch the execution. They arrived early to get a good view and they stayed to the God-denying end. The boy was morose all the way home. His father watched him slyly out of the corner of his eye. As soon as they reached Leeds, William Shent slowly, silently, deliberately, fetched out the strap that he used for sharpening his barber's razors. The ten-year-old boy watched, frightened but resigned. His father had not said a word since the execution, letting it engrave itself upon his son's memory. Now he talked about sin, carefully and inhumanly like a priest droning a litany: how one might be called away at any moment by Death with one's sins unforgiven — a sudden accident, a seizure of the heart — to face an eternity of torment. Then he coldly and methodically thrashed his son to make all these lessons stick. When the man had finished he was covered in a fine sweat, just as in his barber's shop when he was nervous of a rather grand customer. The boy knew better than to cry but he trembled all over. Afterwards his father pointed out how brief his punishment had been, compared to Eternity. Then John was put in his bedroom with shutters and door locked. The total darkness, like the darkness of Eternity, made his head spin. The child who had been brought up to say "God" as the first word that he uttered forgot his pains in his fear of death and he prayed for forgiveness of his sins even though he didn't understand quite what they were. His nails gripped his palms so tightly that they almost bled. Suppose death came suddenly tomorrow when he had committed more sins and had not time for an extra dose of forgiveness? Out of sheer fear of dying, the child prayed to be taken at this very moment and thus get it over with.

Mary Hepton lived alone when she was free of her husband. John Shread visited her. After indecisively hovering between Mary and his own wife, Shread's problem was solved by a dream. He was being pursued by soldiers, hunted for a crime against men although he did not know what it was. He escaped by piloting a flat, slow boat along a canal which just fitted his barge between its banks. He had a feeling of peace whilst he glided past the soldiers who did not suspect that he could be in this huge boat. But unfortunately the canal came to an end at a narrow conduit with a small iron door. Shread opened it and saw a great manufactory where felled trees were being sliced. The canal had turned aside into waterfalls and a chaotic river where his barge could not follow. Meanwhile an army spread across a plain was coming towards him. He decided to trick them by walking back through them — surely they would not expect this. But turning back was fatal because he found himself driven to the edge of a cliff where he could not escape being driven over.

Shread interpreted this dream as follows. The crime he had committed against men was his defiance of their religion in turning to Mary. His safe peaceful conduct upon water was his being carried by woman. The manufactory was man's alternative to the female way, and Shread's turning back, instead of following the natural course to he brink of which woman had led him, was his dreadful mistake which only returned him screaming over the cliff into the abyss of original creation. He decided to take warning from his dream and urn to Mary. One sunny day in winter when frost locked the landscape at night whilst the birds struggled looking for food during a few sunny hours of the day, he went to her cottage which stood in an oak wood. Her rooms were a mess of unwashed pottery, stale food, stained wooden dishes and untidy clothes, together with rusting ools and chips of stone from her deceased husband's quarry-work. Chickens wandered in and out of the door to roost in Mary's bedroom, even upon her Bible which was as marked with chicken dirt as t was with annotations, many of them furiously scribbled out after she had changed her mind.

"You must perform the twelve labours of Hercules for me — as Hercules did for Omphale the Queen of Lydia," she said. "Hercules cleaned the stables of Augeas and picked up the excrement of the Stymphalian birds. After each labour you will be rewarded with my body." When he did not refuse, she undressed in front of him, climbed into her bed and read her Bible, ignoring him whilst he picked things up from the floor, contrived places to put them and, when there was enough space to be able to clean, swept it and went out with buckets to the half-frozen spring. After he had finished, they made love in the mid-afternoon whilst the blackbirds, robins and thrushes sang a few thin pre-spring songs. Whilst the lovers rested peacefully afterwards she said, "Get rid of your wife and come to live with me. You will be surrounded always by such a clear golden light of happiness as you have never imagined nor no man has known since the Goddess Diana died."

Back in his own home Shread watched his wife as she peeled rushes to make the lights that they gave to the church in return for the grass in the churchyard. A mass of dark green rushes were on the floor by her chair and a bundle of the white naked-looking wicks that emerged after the outer layers had been peeled away were laid side by side on the table top. The deftness required for this job, one which she had done since she was a child, came to her as naturally as singing to a bird, and she was now teaching their three-year-old daughter to make rush-lights. Meanwhile John Shread wrote a verse on a scrap of paper on his knee:

> "While savage winter all his fury play'd,
>   Tho' round my house, he rag'd with all his powers,
>   I musing sat, and sung away mine hours:
>   Yea, the day long, and in each evening gloom,
>   I meditated in the sounding loom;
>   Meanwhile I wove the flow'ry waved web,
>   With fingers colder than the icy glebe;
>   And oftentimes thro' the whole frame of man,
>   Bleak chilling horrors, and a sickness ran."

His wife was unable to read it and anyway did not wish to know wha
he had written: being a poet's wife had not rewarded her.

Shread knew that another man loved his wife more than he himsel
did, and there was a custom for solving this problem. "I'm going to
sell you," he said.

She raised her breast in a heavy sigh, without looking at him. "No
in my own town," she pleaded.

"Wherever tha chooses."

"No nearer than Hebden Bridge."

"Just as tha likes. You must go all the way wi' a rope around thy
neck, otherwise it wouldn't be legal."

With trembling fingers she peeled another rush. "It's that Mary
Hepton. You are her slave. Everyone knows it." He blushed
"You might well hang your head, John. But it is your nature, as
some are, it can be seen in your eyes. I'll see that woman hung as a
witch!"

"Imagine that I have died," John said.

"It would be better if you had. For now you have killed mine
and your daughter's love for you — a more precious thing than your
own life." But she was not sorry to have at last arrived at this
divorce.

She insisted on tying her own noose, and fastened it quite tight so
as to cause her a little suffering, and with a lead six feet long to keep
Shread away from her. She made her husband tie her hands in front
of her to walk for ten miles behind him over the moors. Shread put
her up for auction at the foot of the bridge. Everyone already knew
who in Hebden Bridge wanted her, and being a popular man no-one
bid against him. For five shillings Shread's wife went to her lover.
And Shread went to his. Mary Hepton made him bring the noose
that he had used and she herself burnt it. She took Shread into her

100

bed and they both made love more times than ever before for either of them. She cried at each orgasm, except for the last ones because by then they were both sore. Then they turned back-to-back for sleep, but when they awoke they found themselves in one another's arms.

Chapter 8

WILLIAM GRIMSHAW GAVE most of Elizabeth's legacy of silks, caps, stockings and petticoats to Molly, although Sarah's clothes still remained a secret hoard in a rarely-opened chest. The servant — who returned to her place by Grimshaw's fireside and spent her evenings letting out the dresses to fit her plumpening body — was now William's main companion, John and Jane having been taken away once again after their stepmother's death to stay with their grandfather at Ewood. At first Molly only wore these dresses during the evenings, but before long she was draggling Elizabeth's silks around kitchen and farm. Her days were cycles of the same petty activities and the domestic trivialities irritated William. "As soon as Molly steps into Heaven she will think it's her duty to start scrubbing the floors," he thought. He escaped from the stifling atmosphere as often as he could. He had become the leader of the Methodists' Yorkshire circuit and was now as much an itinerant as William Darney — often taking Maskew or another preacher with him. As the better weather came on he might be away for a week, usually travelling on foot for the sake of the company he met and for the chances of evangelising along the way, for though he was a big man he had short legs and he rolled along with a gait so unlike a gentleman that people were not put off chatting to him on the road. Once he had dressed more like a tradesman than a parson, and now he looked most like a farmer impatient to get to market. Leaving on Monday, he set off to Bradford, then Halifax, and back along the Calder Valley to Hebden Bridge, to reach Haworth for Saturday. Another week he would go to Heptonstall and Todmorden, preaching in farms at Mankinholes and Dobroyd.

These local gatherings he did in winter. He was rarely offered church pulpits and more often he conducted services in farm kitchens — speaking of the evils of the flesh and the tortures of Hell under ceilings hung with hams, whilst pigs and other beasts copulated noisily in the yard or in the barn beyond a partition wall. When summer came Grimshaw went by horse further afield, sleeping happily in rough accommodation and bearing some abuse from the crowds. Eventually his travels took him throughout Yorkshire, Northumberland, Lancashire, Cheshire, Derbyshire, Rutland and Lincolnshire. The deaths of his wives encouraged this wandering. He was busy as if trying to forget something, and when you talked to him you felt that you had only half arrested his flight. His features had a look of having been boiled in a cauldron — he was more like a force of maddened nature than a man.

Grimshaw also travelled to Newcastle in the north and southwards to Sheffield, Rotherham and Doncaster. He went along the valley of the River Don, which the Celts had named after the goddess Diana of their Mediterranean homeland. Thus the parson took his own God to kill the pagan goddess in her Yorkshire home. He passed by enclosures of the wheat that had once wrapped the Celtic tribute sent to Delos. The wheat fields had a sheen with a crimson path across them as they reflected the setting sun; the breeze was heated upon the corn and it wrapped him in a warm smell as he passed by. Grimshaw felt no special emotions about this and when he saw the little figures made of straw (people who knew him hid them from his sight) he thought only of "superstition".

Grimshaw often had to address meetings at four o'clock in the morning, before his congregation went to work. His arrival could not be relied upon; sometimes he was prevented by bad weather whilst at other times he was called back for a funeral and found that his parishioner was not yet dead, and it was a trick to keep him in his own parish. His Methodist congregations often missed their work for a preacher who could not get there on time. In some places they had to meet in secret. As soon as Grimshaw was seen on the horizon, a white sheet was spread over a bush and the Methodists then left their farms, their looms and tools and were seen hurrying across the moor.

Molly made up parcels of bread and cheese, preserved meat and pickles for him. The servant was twenty-four and William was thirty-eight, yet she mothered him. There was nobody else in her life. She was not very pretty and was without a dowry. As she lovingly watched the evangelist depart — through snow, buttercups, or mud that seemed to suck him warningly back from the mouth of a rainstorm — Molly remembered how long ago she had been sent down from her parents' cottage on Todmorden Edge, half-starved and baffled by the banging of cottage looms and the noise of thirteen

103

brothers and sisters; how she had been like a hungry field-mouse creeping out of the hill grass and had found a home with Parson Grimshaw. Grimshaw was her fate.

"You might do some good for trade through your evangelising," John Greenwood said, showing all his teeth in a bland smile one philosophical evening over Grimshaw's teapot. He laughed and spat tobacco juice. "The advancement of trade is prevented by the people's superstitions. Robert Greenwood has been looking many years for coal in Heptonstall. Now that he has come to where he might find it, the common people will not dig because they say that King Arthur is asleep under the hill. There are gentlemen wanting to open a turnpike who cannot do so because of superstitions about removing old boulders and stone columns that lie in the way. I know a clothier yonder who may not dam the river to build a mill because they say that lovers were drowned there in ancient days. You might do some great good by curing the countryside of barbaric customs."

So Grimshaw set out to disinfect the landscape: he became obsessed with cleaning the whole countryside and the souls of those who dwelled in it. He went to "regulate" (as he put it) Hardibutts Farm — now like Heptonstall in the hands of the Methodists, whilst Darney had been made a circuit preacher. As Grimshaw walked amongst the barns and cowsheds, conversing with Amos and Mary Lightowler about religion and agriculture, the price of corn and of redemption, William saw hung above the cows a circular stone the size of a household quern, with a hole in its centre. It was there to protect the cattle against witches' curses. Grimshaw, his conversation suddenly drying up, his face suffused with an onrush of blood and sweat, smashed it on the cobblestones. The Lightowlers, who had blandly answered his questions and calmly offered him ale to wash down his bread and cheese, turned nervous and white. Grimshaw wondered: did sedition — spiritual and therefore perhaps worldly too — lurk in their souls that they shifted from foot to foot, sucked their teeth and stared as if trying to count the blades of grass on the horizon, merely because they were asked a few simple questions about the throne of God in their hearts? William led them indoors and "examined" them more thoroughly. He sat them on low milking stools before a window where they were dazzled in the sunlight, and stood in front of them asking his terrible questions. Grimshaw's key words — "salvation", "forgiveness", "eternity", and "sin" — had become stronger than life itself for him; men were

104

not fortified against their power, particularly if they were uttered from a lofty rock on the moor or from a high oak pulpit; words fat with meaning, they overbore people like the fat bellies of the prosperous. What, Grimshaw asked, did the Lightowlers think would be the everlasting fate of backsliders, of those who had broken faith — oh, how much worse it was than for those who had never known it! His sweaty face came at them like punches out of the sunlight, so close that they flinched. They asked for water but he would not give it to them until they had satisfactorily answered his questions. Time after time they were confused and contradicted themselves.

Mad Grimshaw stood aside at last. The old couple, who had watched the fierce sunlight cross almost the whole span of their window and were still afraid to rise, leant forwards on their uncomfortable stools and rested their sweating foreheads on their hands. As they glanced sideways they saw Grimshaw take a card from his pocket, write their names, sign and date it as a certificate of the satisfactory state of their souls. "We'll 'appen do, then?" Amos Lightowler said, feeling weak, but smiling, gentle, kindly and unwilling to admit that he would be relieved to see Parson Grimshaw depart.

As well as other preachers, or apprentice preachers like Jonathan Maskew, Grimshaw often took his daughter Jane on these hikes. At the age of ten her forehead already wore a frown. All her experiences, culminating in watching her stepmother snatched with a grovelling last-minute recantation from tumbling straight into the pit of Hell, had robbed Jane of her spontaneity. The child had a habit of not looking one in the face and affected all the sickly mannerisms taught by the women who had surrounded her since birth. Her father therefore had great hopes for her soul. "She has at last begun to show a serious concern for her sinful state," he wrote to John Wesley. He also liked to take John Shent with him. Ever since Ben Rushworth's execution the boy had been in the same state of quivering uncertain soul as Jane. To Grimshaw's mind he was a better companion for her than her own brother John, who grew more intractable, sullen and resentful every day.

Grimshaw was full of tricks to delight the children with. There was a farmer who boasted about his charity; once Grimshaw turned up on his doorstep as night fell, with himself and the children disguised as beggars. What laughs they had when the farmer discovered that he had turned his own parson from the door! Another cottager who had

105

not been to church hid up his chimney when he saw Grimshaw coming. Mad Grimshaw marched into the cottage, as usual without knocking, saw a few grains of soot sifting down into the fireplace, crept forwards silently and bellowed up the chimney, "Old Nick has come to thee for thy sins!" so that the poor man wet himself with fright.

One spring evening they walked across the common together. They were surrounded by a delicious smell of charred moorland as the heather was burnt to make way for the new shoots. The sky was a white blaze behind the faint smoke screening the sun. Jane watched the larks running with their crests bobbing in the new grass. When a patch of the shifting sunlight broke through and fell upon one of them, it rose and a few feet above the ground began singing, ascending higher and higher, in its short pauses clutching its wings against its body in ecstasy, and trembling until it was but a dot like a black star in a white sky. Jane lifted her face from its usual contemplation of the ground and she followed the bird's rise until she lost it. In her bright eyes you could see her thrill as she searched. She suddenly, for a moment only, looked like her mother; she had her mother's alert stance, ready for something to be delighted by or to laugh at. Grimshaw felt the vision stab at his chest. He remembered how until Sarah died he had on sunny afternoons — and even in winter when the sky was blue — lain on his back and watched the larks as they pierced and skimmed the surface of heaven. The thirty-nine-year-old man realised that he had lost his joy in the world.

They were on their way to visit an old woman who was almost blind and lived alone at the edge of the common. The cataracts upon her eyes made the light unbearable. She was permanently stooped from avoiding it and she came out only at dusk to feed her hens and milk her cow. Her bat-like flittings made the villagers think she was a witch who turned herself into a vampire that sucked the blood of cattle and of maidens — Jane imagined that she must be something like the Pope. (Jane had no clear idea as to whether the leader of the Catholic Church was man, woman or beast, nor even how many legs or heads the monster had.) Because of her fear of being taken for a witch, the woman came over-regularly to church and did everything she could to show her piety. But John Grimshaw told his father that the old woman still cursed like a sailor whenever the children teased her. So William came to test her. They found her stumbling along the edge of the common, banging a piece of wood on a stone to call her

106

hens together. William poked at her from behind with a stick. As he had suspected, she cursed him sufficient to make him wonder whether to have the old hag do a public penance in church.

William's most forceful way of trying to persuade his children into an overwhelming sense of their own sinfulness was to take them to witness deathbed confessions. John Grimshaw almost enjoyed these visits. He spent much of his time helping Maskew slaughter pigs. John insisted on holding the bucket under their cut throats, then he stirred the blood to prevent it becoming lumpy and took it indoors to Molly to watch her mix it with flour, sage and thyme, roll it into balls and bake "blood pudding". John did not feel pity: the messy deaths of old people, their revolting ways of eating, drinking and urinating, seemed to hypnotise the eleven-year-old boy. His feelings were in suspense, as they were when he tortured a frog or watched the farmers slaughter their animals. He felt absolutely no fear of death. When he saw his father, in a rage at a funeral service, swear "There is every reason to believe that the soul which once enlivened this clay is now in Hell!" and bang rhythmically on the lid of the coffin so that the mourners flinched at every word, John loved it although Jane went white with fear.

Like his father, John wandered the hills alone; but he went (as William Grimshaw had done when he was a young man) to hunt animals and birds with his father's old gun or to brood in the moorland hollows. He made friends with the Pighells family. It was what was called "close" — it admitted few people into its secrets. Their servants were the tight-lipped silent kind and the walls were for ever being made higher around the Pighells' estate. Their tenter frames were in hidden enclosures where one could not see how much the cloth was being stretched — which scandalised a most basic principle of the neighbourhood, but no-one could do anything about it. The Pighells held cock-fights in the kitchen yard, sometimes they baited a bear and once they killed a bull tied in a stream.

During Easter 1747, John Wesley came on horseback into Yorkshire, mainly to visit Parson Grimshaw. His opinion of the West Riding was that it held the most barbaric people in England — and that was his reason for liking it. "The North of England suits me best, where so many are groaning for redemption," he wrote, and he penetrated further into Yorkshire's valleys than had any other gentleman-preacher. He was used to struggling, almost from birth.

In Epworth, Lincolnshire, where he had been born the son of the rector, he had been brought up in an embattled atmosphere. The parishioners, angry with the gentry for draining the marshes, had maimed the rector's cattle and twice burned down the Rectory — John Wesley always described himself as "a brand plucked from the burning". Within the home his father Samuel quarrelled bitterly with his strong-minded mother Susanna over such things as her refusal to say "Amen" to a prayer for King William III (for she had come from a Dissenting family). When she continued to refuse, he vowed divine vengeance upon himself if he ever slept with her again. Whilst she scandalised her husband by conducting services for peasants and servants on the unconsecrated ground of her own kitchen — with such success that there were more people crowded in there on Sunday mornings than were in the church — Samuel avoided his parishioners by spending ten years writing a Latin dissertation on the Book of Job and also a *Life of Jesus Christ* in nine thousand lines of heroic metre (which earned him a place in Pope's Temple of Dullness in *The Dunciad*). Susanna gave birth to thirteen children. Having to keep the house quiet, she treated the ones who lived brutally. "When turned a year old (and some before) they were taught to fear the rod, and to cry softly, by which means they escaped abundance of correction . . . and that most odious noise of crying children was rarely heard in the house . . . ." she wrote. John had been brought up surrounded by women, with five elder sisters, cosseted by female servants and recognising his mother as the strongest presence in the family. Though a gentleman he was tiny and thin, dressed in neatly-tailored dark clothes, without a wig and having long dark hair parted around his sensitive face, which had a hooked nose, thin tremulous lips and hanging cheeks. He looked cadaverous enough to be a poet — particularly next to Grimshaw, as they stood in the Sowdens porch, both smiling benignly in return for the sunny spring landscape which God had laid out before them.

"A more beauteous prospect I have rarely seen — the fruitful hills and woods on either hand. And yet, Mr Grimshaw, will not the thought often intrude upon your happy parishioners that they must in the end leave this paradise — these happy woods and mountains fit for gods?"

"They know it well, and I think the inhabitants of this region have now more sense of utility than of beauty."

It struck Wesley that there were few of these inhabitants to be seen. "They are all in town watching a spectacle," Grimshaw told him sourly. "Such a grip these things have on a still-barbarous people — I can't even keep my own son away from them. The worst in the neighbourhood are caught up in it. We should go there ourselves and see what good we might do."

As they came into town there was indeed a crowd watching the Easter "Pace Egg Play". The audience was year by year composed more of Methodists come to enjoy the bad consciences of the others. At the sight of Grimshaw and this stranger, "I told yee! I told yee!" the Methodists shouted gleefully to young men whose faces were flushed with drink, and to girls who had bits of ribbon in their hair and were sometimes showing their ankles. Grimshaw however motioned them to be quiet, for he wanted John Wesley to witness the worst that Haworth had to offer. The performance might now have come to a standstill, had not the main character — Saint George, defeater of the powers of nature and darkness — been taken by Thomas Pighells: wrapped in clattering bits of metal, waving a sword, he leapt heavily and clumsily into the arena, almost tripping over his clogs and bawling out his verses.

> "I am St George who from Old England sprung,
> My famous name throughout the world has rung!
> Many bloody deeds and wonders have I known,
> And made false tyrants tremble on their thrones.
> I followed a fair lady to the giant's gate,
> Confined in dungeon deep to meet her fate.
> There I resolved, with true knight errantry,
> To burst the door and set the prisoner free.
> When lo! A giant almost struck me dead,
> But by my valour I cut off his head!
> I've sought the world all round and round,
> But a man to equal me I've never found."

"That disgusting fellow there," Grimshaw said to Wesley, "is a clothier who recently exported to Russia cartloads of cloth that he had overstretched on the tenter frames to make more money from them. So after they had been made into uniforms for the Imperial Army they shrank on parade in the first shower of rain. A villain who reduced the Russians to bursting their buttons and moving their arms like puppets!"

All the main parts were taken by men and boys. (In pagan times they had been priests.) Now John Shread, dressed in tattered clothes and playing the part of "Slasher", came into the ring and shouted, "I'm the man to equal thee!"

"And who'rt thou?" Thomas Pighells challenged. They circled about each other, banging their swords together and stamping their clogs on the cobblestones until they'd nearly forgotten the play that they were performing. Then Shread remembered to recite:

> "I am a valiant soldier,
> Bold Slasher is my name,
> With sword and buckle by my side
> I hope to win the game!
>
> And for to fight with me, St George,
> I see thou art not able,
> For with my trusty broadsword
> I soon would thee disable."

"Disable! Disable!" Pighells exclaimed, thrusting his shoulders back and strutting about.

> "It lies not in thy power!
> For with my trusty broadsword I soon will thee devour.
> Stand back, Slasher, and let no more be said,
> For if I draw my glittering sword
> I'm sure to break thy head!"

> "How canst thou break my head
> Since my head is made of iron,
> My hands and feet of knuckle bone?
> I challenge thee to field!"

Pighells, so much bigger than Shread, bore down on him as if he was going to crush him. At the same time he challenged the eye of Wesley who, used to grasping strange situations quickly, sized him up as his major enemy in this town — a filthy fellow, and the personification of worldly darkness. The actors banged their swords together until Shread lay on the ground and the crowd cheered: "Shready's done for!" Shread squealed, laughing, "A doctor! A doctor! Five pounds for a doctor! Who'll go fetch a doctor?"

The doctor entered with a bag of gold in one hand and a jar of blood in the other, which he kept spilling onto the ground like the

Haworth apothecary. Wesley however took this to be an insult to his own healing of the sick. His anger began to boil but Grimshaw restrained him to see the rest of this absurd performance. The "doctor" rushed about, harrassed, mopping his forehead and saying,

> "In comes I who never came yet!
> With my great head and little wit!"

"How far have you travelled in doctorship?" Slasher asked him.

> "Fromt' fireside, cupboard and into bed
> Where I eat my cheese and bread
> That makes my nose and cheeks so red.
> From Italy, 'Eptonstall, Germany, France and Spain
> And now returned to cure old England again!"

"What diseases can you cure?" Slasher asked.
"All sorts."
"What's all sorts?"

> "The itch, the stitch, the palsy and the gout.
> If a man's got nineteen devils in his soul
> I can cast twenty out. . . ."

The doctor, jangling his money, made as if to bleed Slasher. But Slasher got up and was chased out of the ring. Finally "Old Tosspot" came in — this was John Grimshaw, his face blackened with soot, carrying a basket full of eggs that were coloured red and dragging a straw-stuffed effigy of a woman. It was now William Grimshaw's turn to be choleric, realising that his son had sneaked from home to prepare for this. "What does think of yon?" he was asked by one of his parishioners who mischievously sidled up. Grimshaw's answer was drowned by the fiddle played deliberately, it seemed, in his ear whilst all the actors in the ring sang:

> "Oh the next that steps in's
> The old toss-pot you see,
> He's a gallant old man
> And he has a degree.
> He's a stick in his hand
> An' he wears a pigtail
> And he takes his delight
> In drinking strong ale!"

111

The whole town was this day boiling with antagonism to Grimshaw, and now that they had overcome the surprise of his appearing here, after which nothing had happened, the confidence in their liberation was growing.

John Grimshaw danced around the ring, giving his eggs to the people in the audience and singing:

> "I've some eggs in my basket,
>   Although I appear
>   Expecting some time
>   To come in for my share.
>   Although I am ragged
>   And not so well dressed,
>   I can kiss some bonny lasses
>   As well as the best.
>
>   They powdered my hair
>   With a dredging tin box,
>   And I've got a pigtail
>   And you see how it cocks.
>   I've a stick in my hand
>   And a pipe in my spout
>   And an old tally-wife
>   Who is better than nowt."

However, he dared not approach his father and John Wesley, so Pighells grabbed the basket and went up to the preachers. This was too much for Wesley. Having made sure that he was standing in an elevated place, he looked Pighells directly in the eye. "Are *you* prepared to die?" he asked sonorously.

Pighells became shifty, his armour rustling quietly but audibly in the silent street. Wesley now addressed everyone. He fixed his eye on one person at a time, quelling the most rebellious-looking before moving on to others.

"Have you gone mad? Such noise! Is it a feast day? A feast of Bacchus? Or Venus? Or Belial? In good Mr Grimshaw's parish? Oh shame on you! Shame, shame on a Christian country! What a weight of sin lies on this nation! The sloth and indolence! The luxury and sensuality! Even Solomon knew nothing of such abominations! In the open streets they play as if at the theatre. They buy and sell even on the Lord's Day! Money is their god and gain their godliness!"

112

No-one could answer him and after proving himself through the following silence, he led the company in prayers and hymns.

Wesley stayed at Sowdens that night — when John Grimshaw received the sound thrashing that he deserved. Grimshaw, John Wesley and Molly sat around the fireside until late, discussing how to civilise Mr Grimshaw's Yorkshire where dissenting and political sects were breeding "like verminous life in a pond" and breaking up the Methodists. Whilst the evangelists drank tea, the logs dropped in the grate and were replaced, sending rushes of light over the shadowy walls. There was a brooding electric atmosphere as if a thunderstorm was threatening. When they went outside to piss under the brittle stars, they brought up fertile smells from the hot spring earth. In the uncanny silence and clarity, some frightened geese sent their sharp screams clear as bells across the valley and a dog howled eerily as if it was the eve of the Day of Judgement. It seemed an ominous time to be discussing the conversion of Yorkshire.

The next morning Grimshaw took Wesley to Hardibutts Farm. On the way they passed the open door of a farmhouse, where the farmer sat within neglecting his work whilst he suffered a nose-bleed. Wesley stopped, told him to sniff vinegar up his nose and to apply it to his neck, face and temples. This Christ-like healing being completed, the preachers pressed on towards the moors. The sky was clear blue. In the enclosures under the rows of cloth, camomile daisies were in flower and the earliest buttercups were lifting still-unopened yellow globes. New walls had been built even since Grimshaw had last been here, only a week ago. "Eventually all the moors will be bound in the long chains of the walls and with God's help will be bent to the service of man!" William said. There was a staggering improvement taking place both in man's material success and in his moral welfare. Everywhere the grass was shooting up fast and it bent in silver ripples under the wind.

The sunlight was too hard and bright to last and they saw indigo clouds thrusting up on the horizon. A moor guide, whom they met on his return from seeing someone over to Lancashire, warned them not to go on. The parsons reminded the youth that they were all in God's hands and the boy, old beyond his years — a cloth-dresser's apprentice — smiled cynically and hurried on downhill. Before they had reached Sun Hill the sky had darkened totally and a sudden eerie wind swept over them, so strong and unaccountable that it might have been a ghost. Then the first large white drops of rain hit them. The storm came in a rush. The moor was so soaked that their horses stuck and slithered in mud, where a few minutes before it had been as dry as rock. The heather and whinberry that had rustled drily now hissed against the horses' legs. The two men pulled their hats down to their eyebrows and bent their heads in the shelter of the horses' necks. Lightning slashed the dark sky. Thunder rolled. Then suddenly there was an explosion that made their mounts bolt. Glancing with painfully screwed-up eyes across the moor, where the rocks and the beaten heather gleamed like pewter, the two preachers saw a jet of fire bursting out of a hill near Denholme. It was an explosion in a coal pit. Dark specks could be seen thrusting upwards in the flames. Rocks, no doubt — but sometimes these pit explosions had scattered the limbs and bodies of colliers over the moor.

Down in the valley they could see Hardibutts Farm, and the storm rained weaker blows as they descended. As they came within sight of the farm, they saw someone dash out and drape a white sheet upon a rowan tree. Men and women came running over the moor towards the farmhouse. They were in their working dress just as the call had taken them, in cowhouse or before the loom and spinning wheel, coats or improvised rags thrown over them as protection from the storm. As the preachers reached Hardibutts, pausing in the barn to shake water from their hats and cloaks, they could hear that the loft above was packed. Grimshaw led the way up the ladder. Raising his head into the loft he saw Darney, red-faced, drunk and almost naked, sitting with two women, also nearly undressed. One of them was Mary Hepton, her thin little breasts dangling like dried fruit out of her dress. The cattle beneath, the rush-lights in the windowless loft, and the bodies packed close together in the straw, made the place hot and stuffy and Darney's face ran with sweat.

"Come up, Master Wesley, Master Grimshaw," Darney said, waving a flask at them. "Did you witness the fire on the hill? We are expecting the end of the world this night, and the beginning of the next world tomorrow. This is the Millennium and I am Christ that is come amongst you."

Wesley had met scenes like this before. His first calm glance around the room noted the positions of the women with the men; particularly where there were two women with one man. This alone told him that they were a sect of Antinomians — apart from the fact that so many were naked. The Lightowlers had disappeared.

114

Everyone else was impervious to what Grimshaw and Wesley might think, even though the Darneyites had gathered the previous evening to discuss the visit by the two leaders of Methodism. Amos and Mary Lightowler had led that meeting and everything was being conducted in a fairly orderly way. Then Darney appeared unexpectedly, having found his way across the moor by the brilliant starlight. He came in raving about the beauty of the stars and he was slightly drunk. He brought Mary Hepton a present of a small silver box that he had obtained from an Arab in Manchester. "Inside it is the foreskin of Christ," Darney said. Mary opened it and saw lying on blue velvet a scrap of white half-transparent skin, not quite shrivelled up and looking like a hen's fresh turd. "Kiss it beforehand and it will guarantee you will be fertile," he said.

"One who suffers, hopes. And one who hopes, believes," Mary answered.

"Tis a true foreskin! Yon Arab was a travelled man. He told me of places where men wear false breasts and have been operated on so that they must squat like women to pass water."

A man named Abraham Ingham, whose whole face and body were tattooed with snakes, swords, birds, animals and dragons, and who travelled the fairs displaying himself stage by stage in order to hold the attention of a crowd whilst he preached to them the Gospel of Christ and the world's end said, "I have travelled the whole world and have seen it in many barbarous countries. It is true!"

Then Darney declared, "I have altered my mind about handing over to the Wesleys. It has been announced to me by signs that the Millennium will dawn tomorrow, and I alone must lead the Chosen into glory. First of all there will be fire upon the hills, and the furniture of the Elect will be shaken by angels."

The Lightowlers fled, scared out of their wits, to stay with neighbours. Amongst those who remained, their belief that the end of the world had come had the same effect as drunkenness. Those who were usually mild became aggressive. The sad became foolishly merry. The happy were now melancholic. The timid were reckless and carefree. Just as by mid morning of the next day they were beginning to weary and lose faith, there came the fire on the hill and the angels rattled Hardibutts Farm.

What a smell there was in the loft by the time that Grimshaw and Wesley got there! A man was being sick, careless of where it fell. Mary Hepton, her cheeks flushed and her limbs trembling as she lay in the straw with Darney, saw the visitors' disgust and said, "The nakedness of man is the handiwork of God. Take off your clothes and pray with us!" Abraham Ingham approached Grimshaw with a piece of dried plant that he had been stroking under his nose, put it to Grimshaw's face and said, "Sniff this herb and you will see God more clearly!" The biting smell made Grimshaw dizzy and he twitched at the closeness of the purple dragons upon Ingham's cheeks. John Wesley with his face also aflame made to speak and Mary Hepton stopped him by lifting her skirt and petticoat above her thighs. She was naked underneath and Darney's semen dribbled out of her. "This is the way for Christ to enter in!" she cried. The two preachers were then confused by being asked ridiculous questions, such as, "Do angels have to eat? What do they feed upon?" Darney said with authority, "Heaven and Hell are not places. They are inward states of the soul. These are the last days. We are the chosen. We may do as we like, we are still the chosen and there's nowt anyone can do 'bout that! The Elect *are* the Elect!"

Wesley and Grimshaw eventually insisted upon some light in the place. This in itself sobered everyone. Through the opened shutters it could be clearly seen that the storm had died down without the world having been torn to pieces. A farmer and his wife were climbing a moorland track with bales upon their backs, taking their week's weaving to the Heptonstall Piece Hall. The two Methodist leaders first of all struggled to get everyone to dress decently, separating the men from the women on either side of the room. John Wesley recommended several of them to take electric shocks for their hysteria. "Sit on a cake of rosin, submit to electrification for thirty minutes morning and night." Then the preachers led the company in prayers for the King. "Is he one of the Elect? We will not pray for him if he isn't," Darney grumbled.

"There will be no *revolution* to save the world!" John Wesley began. "Man must save himself from within. When the heart of each of us is cleansed of sin then the world will become a better place and man will be free."

"To sin is to be free!" Mary Hepton shouted.

"We cannot sin! We are the Elect!" Abraham Ingham said.

William Darney was falling asleep. Others also slept. Abraham Ingham started snoring. More people stumbled down the ladder to be sick upon the sodden fields. The sun shone, not oppressively or threateningly but glittering beautifully in many rainbows amongst

116

the water on the grass blades. The air was light. Blackbirds, thrushes and robins were singing in the hawthorns and the rowans whilst larks rose confidently into the sky above the moors and mocked the Apocalypse.

John Wesley gave advice to the sleepy, sickly congregation on how to be good Methodists. "Fast every Friday. Deny yourself every useless pleasure of sense, imagination and honour. Eat no flesh nor late suppers. Do not ramble up and down but go where directed by your class leader and there only." Grimshaw distributed his little cards to those of the Darney Society who were now admitted as Methodists. Amos Lightowler had crept back to his farm and flock, and was appointed class leader. Wesley told them all to endeavour always to be serious, weighty and solemn in deportment, and to "sing no hymns of your own composing". At this point Darney left, muttering angrily to himself a quotation from the Book of Daniel: "When the transgressors are come to the full, a King of fierce countenance and understanding dark sentences shall stand up," until he was out of hearing, banging into the tenters of cloth and splashing carelessly through the stream.

He stumbled through valleys and across the hills, and almost reeling with tiredness now he burst over Whirlaw where he could see over the deep cleft of the Calder Valley. He had a vision such as so many others in Yorkshire were nowadays receiving from God. The sun was about to set upon Flower Scar Hill, throwing gold all about him, and a deep purple-blue shadow, like a pool of unfathomable water, into the valley. Darney felt that the dimly seen trees and houses below him were a great crowd of people who were screaming because Satan was coming. "By God's Grace I will turn neither to right hand nor to left for him!" Darney shrilled, waving his arms about on the hill top. Then he saw the Devil: at first no more than a red speck in Darney's eye, soon clearly a gigantic red bull coming from his left out of Todmorden and running through the crowd as a beast through standing corn. Yet Satan did not bother any of them, but came charging up the hill straight towards Darney as if he would gore him through the heart. "Lord help me!" Darney shouted. As the impetus of that flying weight fell upon him he grabbed the bull by the horns, with one mighty heave twisted him over onto his back, and set his own right foot on the Devil's neck. Then he shouted across the valley to all those thousands of people, "Now cry to Jesus that what you have seen me perform, He will enable you to do!" He seemed to

117

wake up the stones on the far side of the valley with the echo. A boy herding some sheep, who had watched the red haired preacher struggling, sweating, dancing about, finally took fright and, deserting his sheep, fled down the hillside. This awoke Darney from his vision, his legs so weak that he had to lean against one of the fantastic stones on Whirlaw, with the sweat dripping coldly down his neck and cooling his chest.

The sun had now set. Everywhere was a dull twilit grey as Darney hurried off to stay overnight with his disciples in Todmorden. They listened devoutly to his tale of the world's end that would have come had he not averted it by his struggle with the bull Satan, and afterwards they all prayed together; but still his simple congregation could not understand why Mr Wesley and Mr Grimshaw, being undoubtedly men of God, had not become Darney's followers. Unsoothed, Darney finally went home to Bacup. The roof of his barn had collapsed. His wife saw that he was angry enough without this extra burden; as he stretched before the fire she unfastened his boots and brought him ale. "Have you had a good tour?" she asked timidly. He was half asleep and he opened one eye. "Nothing much this time," he told her (it was useless to talk to his wife). "Them at Hardibutts spending money like drunken weavers on hay for Mr Wesley's horse and wine for preachers. The Devil is coming to Yorkshire in this guise! I shall go up to Scotland for a while out of his way." The next morning he left his eldest son to repair the barn whilst he himself set off to convert Scotland.

From Hardibutts John Wesley was taken to Heptonstall where he had a similar scene with the Darney Society, and to whom he recommended cold baths as a cure for their extravagant expectations of the Millennium. He appointed Robert Greenwood as class leader. Greenwood had been totally ruined by his search for coal in Heptonstall, for he had borrowed large sums of money in expectation of the world coming to an end before his debt fell due, and now it looked as though he might spend the rest of his life in a debtors' prison. Grimshaw and Wesley did not know about this. They merely noticed that Greenwood and his family had lost their former vanity.

There were so many wanting to hear the preachers that Wesley was forced to talk to them in the open air. The hilltop was a natural pulpit. Whilst the sun shone upon Wesley, the valley steeply below became invisible in another storm and turned into a bottomless black hole boiling with rain. Dashes of sunlight, darting between the

118

swiftly flowing clouds, circled upon the hills. "What an emblem of God's taking up the people into a place of safety, whilst the storm falls on all below!" he said.

Grimshaw then hurried Wesley to Ewood, to give John Lockwood absolution before he died. Wesley looked gloomily around the mansion at the statues brought from Italy, France or from barbaric countries, and at the pictures "painted by some of the best artists". "You have a fine house amongst pleasant improvements and a commanding prospect, Mr Lockwood. But does not the thought now intrude: Where will all these be when the earth is burned up? For the good of your soul about to step onto the threshold of Heaven, I would advise you to have those pictures and objects removed into a cellar where they can do no harm. How can your family and servants concentrate upon Eternity in the presence of such seductions? There are some immodest pictures that offend against all decency and common sense. For the good of your soul, I say, have them removed!"

Lockwood agreed, for he did not care much about pictures. He mostly loved the source of his wealth, the manufacture of cloth, particularly of worsteds which were the woollens of the future, and whilst the preachers struggled for the old clothier's soul he advised them to invest in worsteds.

Lockwood could see the demons carved at the edges of the window's drip-stones. These were not so easily removed into the cellars. He pointed at them and squeezed a few words drop by drop out of his strangled throat. "Have I killed and cured the old dragon of the flesh? I think so — long ago, though I've been a terrible sinner."

John and Jane Grimshaw inherited their grandfather's wealth. In the big gloomy house, skinned of its pictures and statues and with black drawn curtains — in the withdrawing room and parlour once set up to be fashionable but which had never echoed with the fun and laughter of a large family of grandchildren, as John Lockwood had hoped; in the cavernous kitchen with Aunt Mary's painted astrological chart fading off the wall — the Grimshaw children helped to go through their grandfather's belongings. They found his pattern book — tiny samples of richly-dyed cloth that his agents took to Amsterdam, whence the patterns dispersed all over the world. (A traveller discovered them woven into rugs made by Peruvian Indians and mistook them for traditional designs, though they were invented by a Yorkshire weaver.) The children found chests full of Spanish

119

coins, clipped guineas and money stamped out by coiners. There were also stacks of promissory notes, like bank notes issued by the coiners as receipts for gold deposited with them for clipping. William Grimshaw pocketed all these for evangelical purposes. John and Jane helped with the great bonfire that was made with the rest of John Lockwood's papers. They jumped into the air to catch bits of charred paper that butterflied away with little flames like wings attached to them. ". . . shalloons provided for St Petersburg to be sent from there to Persia by way of Astracan", they read; "I intend to outdo all England in low priced kerseys", and "We duly recd. ye barrel of excellent oysters".

John Lockwood was given a grand monument in Luddenden churchyard. Nothing could have looked more dynastic and permanent, nevertheless there was carved upon it the words, "We wither as the grass". At the graveside Jane's face was as usual glittering and sweaty, her eyes that shifted from others' gaze were moist and shining and her lips set in a smile like a nun's — melancholic and without mobility, the mask of inward resignation. She said almost nothing. This final death had defeated her. Her light was out. Her father thought that her face shone with the joy of conversion, and discussed with John Wesley where to educate his children before they came into their inheritance. "If you wish to send your daughter headlong into Hell, send her to a fashionable boarding school," Wesley said. As an alternative he suggested his own school at Kingswood near Bristol.

John and Jane, travelling a year later with their father on stage coaches from Keighley, felt so estranged and excited they might have been going to the moon instead of to school. Jane was eleven, John was twelve and they had never before been out of West Yorkshire. Kingswood was a few miles from Bristol amongst forest land that had been smashed and burnt during colliery workings. The colliers' grubby huts stood amongst coal heaps in the forest clearings. There was an air of sulphurous grime as if a valve had been let into foul regions under the earth which ought to be left untapped. The colliers, squatting at doors or at the roadside, or rambling black and tattered through the forest, were malevolent and insolent. John Wesley and Whitefield had set up the school for their benefit but had now taken it over for the children of preachers. It was a mill-like building with rows of plain windows diminishing in size as they rose towards the roof. Wesley had chosen a place in the country because there, he believed, was nothing to delight the senses and so divert the mind's focus upon Eternity: pleasure in looking, in touching or in scents was a sin because if the world were seen to be beautiful one would be unwilling to leave it. The school faced one of the few natural sights from which, John Wesley felt, there was something to be learnt: the setting sun, symbolic reminder of our final descent into Eternity.

John and Jane grasped the situation in a glimpse of the scholars walking through the orderly grounds. They were at the same time studying because no moment was to be spent in play. "He who plays as a child will play as a man," John Wesley said. By reading Isaac Watts' *Divine Songs* and Janeway's *A Token For Children, Being an Exact Account of the Conversion, Holy and Exemplary Lives, and Joyful Deaths of Several Young Children*, the scholars were studying how to die. They were also reading the Classics as selected by John Wesley — leaving out for instance Martial's *Epigrams* and Juvenal's *Satires* because they "shamelessly recommend sodomy and adultery to the young". The pupils were supervised all the time. There was no moment given to play, none without the reminder of death, and every second was supervised — even in the dormitory there was a light burning all night and a master or schoolmistress watching. John and Jane silently observed a sly sullenness and a half-sleeping murderous revolt under the children's eyebrows. These were the offspring of the evangelists who were converting the whole of England.

Jane was eager to do all that was expected of her, to rise promptly as required at four in the morning and follow Charles Wesley's instructions, "As soon as ever you are awake in the morning, dear child, strive as much as you can to keep all worldly thoughts out of your mind". She would earnestly pray to meet her Maker, meanwhile studying the required books, *The Manners of the Ancient Christians* and Law's *Serious Call*, and translating into Latin *The Life of Mr Haliburton*. John's thoughts were less submissive. He weighed up his fellow pupils and decided that he did not like them. He wondered who he might have to knock down with his fists, if only he could get away from the master's eye. But although their reactions were different, both children shared an unutterably hollow feeling when their father left — knowing that he would never come to see them again, according to the rules. Then brother and sister were separated into different buildings.

121

Chapter 9

GRIMSHAW SUFFERED A crisis, which affected the whole town with fear and apprehension as if the Plague had come. Despite his ministry, his crowded church and the purposeful visiting evangelists with Bibles in their pockets, everyone felt how lonely the parson was. Now, just as once before in Todmorden, he grew dizzy whilst preaching his sermon and had to be carried into the graveyard. He lost the feeling in his arms and legs and thought that death was upon him, so he shouted out in terror with his eyes bulging, "Flee to Christ! Abide in Him! With all diligence do it!" before he passed out completely and they took him into the clerk's house. For more than an hour they rubbed his limbs with hot cloths but no life came into them. Meanwhile Grimshaw had a dream. He saw himself in a dark passage, as if between the enclosure walls that John Greenwood was building on the common, and filled with excrement. Behind the wall on the right was Heaven whilst Hell was on the left. In the narrow chink of sky above, during a thunderstorm, Christ argued with God who wanted Grimshaw damned because he had not completely given up his own will. Whilst Grimshaw stuck in the ordure, Christ pleaded for his soul. Then, with fresh blood streaming from his wounds, he thrust down his hands and feet to help the parson into Heaven. At this point the people around felt the warmth coming back into Grimshaw's limbs, he awoke blissfully and was able to return to church to finish his sermon.

At this moment of realising that he had not yet sufficiently given up his will into God's hands, he heard that William Darney had returned from Scotland and was seeking to be re-admitted amongst the Methodists. "Darney is not to be allowed to preach unless he abstains from railing, begging and printing nonsense!" John Wesley insisted. Grimshaw knew that this was too much to expect of Darney. Yet was it not God's will to strive ceaselessly to save even a single soul, no matter what one thought of the body that it inhabited?

122

"Remember the many societies that Darney has founded. If we do not keep them amongst the Methodists, they will cause confusion everywhere," Grimshaw pointed out. Wesley relented a little and said that Grimshaw should examine the state of the pedlar's soul: if it was found satisfactory, he should be put on six months' probation with William Shent set to keep watch over him.

Grimshaw sent for Darney just before the Haworth Fair on July 22nd, at which Darney might have turned up with his pedlar's wares, to the shame of the Methodists. It was hot weather and the country-side stewed in the smells of cut grass. The waterfalls and streams had petered into mere trickles, hardly damping their beds of golden stone. Buzzards gyrated in spiralling currents of air above the moors. The children of Haworth usually hid behind walls and threw stones when pedlars came up the street, but Darney was such a bizarre scarecrow with his wild red hair and his numerous bags that it made them hesitate. Darney grabbed a lad by the ear and asked for the parson. It was only three years after the Scottish uprising and Darney's accent suggested the Devil incarnate; nonetheless, anyone who asked for Grimshaw was sacrosanct. Doubly frightened, the children dropped their stones and pointed, dumbstruck. By the usual magic of village life, news of Darney's errand flew invisibly ahead and nobody harmed him. He was met merely with silent watch-fulness, whilst the coal smoke and the smell of the woolcombers' manure heaps itched in his throat and his footsteps echoed on the stones. He pitied them behind the closed doors of suffocating work-shops and he wondered why more artisans didn't take to field preaching. In other villages, and in Haworth also a few years ago, there was hardly a person to be found on a fine day like this — they would all be out hunting or helping the farmers. Now Parson Grimshaw had disciplined them to ignore the weather and stick to their jobs. Here the women hardly dared even to bring their spinning wheels onto their doorsteps, lest someone describe it as "sinful plea-sure". Darney stopped to let the water of the fountain trickle down his parched throat. The women fell silent and withdrew their buckets, watching him as next he soused his head in the trough. A child tried to speak but his mother cuffed him before he got out a word, and when Darney was a hundred yards further on they started to giggle. The preacher knew better than anyone what it was to be a stranger in a moorland village and he marvelled at the civilising

123

influence of the great Methodist.

Maskew was in the hayfield, raking the grass he had scythed that morning. Grimshaw and Shent together in the study above the porch saw Darney coming, kicking up the hay seeds, the dust-coloured moths and the many-coloured butterflies out of the swathes of hay. In the fierce sunlight his red hair and beard was a halo like the setting sun around his head. Doors and windows were open, and Darney like all visitors to Sowdens walked straight in. The cool stone room relaxed him and the twilight soothed his eyes after the glare of the moor and the hayfields. A small fire burnt, for cooking purposes, and it gave no heat, but it was comforting to stretch before it. He scattered his bags carelessly around him and Molly brought him ale. She admired the reckless Scotsman, and this too made him feel at ease.

He was not surprised that Shent entered with the parson. But his quick suspicions were aroused when Molly was dismissed and the door closed. "Mr Grimshaw, I beg to suggest that there be held quarterly meetings of all the Methodist societies," Darney said.

"To what extent do you believe we are predestined for Heaven or Hell?" Shent interrupted savagely. The barber was a dark figure who melted into the background, whilst Grimshaw commanded the centre of the room.

"Entirely," Darney answered.

"And how must this affect our earthly life?" Grimshaw inquired in a soothing seductive manner.

Darney's response to being questioned was always that of an open-air preacher summoning his wits before an attacking mob. "As our eternal fate is inevitable whatever we do makes no difference, so on earth we may act as we like!" he answered violently and foolishly.

Shent pursed his lips at this blunt declaration of Antinomian doctrine. Its logic was undeniable and its effect was to cause havoc to the discipline of simple people. It opened every door for them. "If a redeemed person does not continue to do good he will lose the grace he has received and will perish eternally!" Grimshaw shouted angrily.

"We are not to say who else will perish and who will not. We know it only of ourselves, in our hearts," Darney answered.

They could all see that their argument would be as unproductive as a clog-fight outside a moorland inn, when men simply bludgeoned one another with sullen kicks. The only way available to the Methodists to attack Antinomian freedom was through such of its spokesmen as Darney, who were the key to its sects, as elusive as moorland mists, but who also were made vulnerable through their weakness for worldly hierarchy and power. Besides, Darney had such good ideas — Grimshaw had noted his suggestion of quarterly meetings, even though he had not appeared to do so.

"You cannot preach those doctrines and be one of our brotherhood. You must surrender to more reasonable arguments," Grimshaw said sweetly. "Your appearance and manner of behaviour must be changed, and brother Shent will supervise your preaching for six months."

Shent shaved off Darney's beard, clipped his hair and fitted him with a wig. In exchange for his pedlar's baggage, the now decent Scotsman was given thirty shillings to help Mrs Darney with her housekeeping. Maskew and other mowers in the fields laughed as Darney left Sowdens, be-wigged, shorn of beard and pedlar's trappings. Shent followed with a pile of red hair, almanacs, printed prophecies, lace and pedlar's bags, and buried them in the manure heap.

Ever since coming to Haworth, Grimshaw had campaigned against the two fairs or "feasts" as they were still called. There was one at which cattle were sold in October and the other for general joyous pedlary was on July 22nd, the Feast of St Mary Magdalene. Grimshaw cursed the reprobates who had waited most of the year for this joyful day, the girls making themselves new dresses and the weavers saving up for new suits. But the parson had little influence because too many outsiders came and amongst these crowds the Haworth natives for a few days let themselves go even more wildly than before Grimshaw set foot in the parish, not caring how sheepishly they had to troop into church the following Sunday.

A week beforehand, when the local weavers were getting their pieces ready, the women were spinning, the craftsmen were making carts, looms, spinning wheels, shoes, suits, furniture to sell and whilst day by day more gypsies, pedlars, alchemists and herbalists moved into Haworth, filling the inn and sleeping on the commons, Grimshaw reminded his congregation that on the Feast of St Mary Magdalene they should be giving thanks for the bringing of a wicked, lascivious, "natural" woman into the disciplines of Christ's church. Hers was an example of how all wild nature through Christian usefulness is brought to serve mankind: "Tears gushed from Mary's eyes as she reflected how basely she had defiled and sought to destroy her own soul. She watered Christ's feet with her tears, wiped them with her hair, most respectfully kissed them and anointed them with rich perfumes and sweet-scented essences. Lord, I pray, open up your Heavens and bring not to pass this coming profanation of the Feast of your saint Mary Magdalene, but flood it out if need be with your own tears, with your storms and rain. . . ."

Grimshaw's praying for rain on the feast brought more fun than any number of conjurers and magic doctors. Many challenged the Mad Parson by sleeping out uncovered on the night before the fair, when it was so dry and warm. But before midnight the stars were put out; the lightning came at dawn and the dry grass was hissing with rain whilst the pools of dust boiled like alchemists' cauldrons. The rain lasted for the whole three days of the fair. Half the main traders had been ruined — an innkeeper for instance who usually sold ten or twelve pounds' sterling of ale had only sold twenty shillings' worth, which barely met his bill for meat.

Now someone — an Irish fiddler whose fiddle had once been smashed by Grimshaw, in the very room in which it was being played — pinned on the church door a drawing of a dead parson swinging in the iron cage on Beacon Hill in Halifax. Mary Hepton, who nowadays "preached" at fairs, braved it in the main square of Haworth to denounce Grimshaw, although she was soon driven off by his parishioners, and the parson saw her go — retaining a curious impression that the bony little woman was like his own Sarah, returned perhaps in the form of an alter-ego, to do evil to him. As Grimshaw passed by, youths hid behind walls and chanted, "I will overturn, overturn, overturn. . . ." The parson heard these menacing words echoing across deserted valleys, not knowing where the voice was hidden. Returning home at twilight down rocky gulleys, he heard "overturn, overturn, overturn," like the melancholy cry of owls, and he — he, Parson Grimshaw — grew afraid of being on the moors alone and he kept clear of the inn. Nonetheless many turned Methodist overnight. Spurred by this success, Grimshaw visited places where neither he nor any other preacher had dared to go before. With Maskew and Paul Greenwood he went to the Piece Hall in Heptonstall, but this was not as successful because the Hall was open only for a couple of mornings each week and there was too much business to be done for them to listen to interfering preachers. Down the length of the room the master clothiers in their best blue, mauve, bottle-green or grey coats and tall black hats, were fondling piles of folded cloth as intently as scholars handling books in a library. All were whispering eerily so that their bargaining could not be overheard. When William Grimshaw with his two nervous friends dared to set himself up on a bench and begin to shout, even that weird murmuring, as of several hundred mice in a barn, stopped and they turned malevolently upon him. They thought that he had come to criticise their little tricks, such as dampening the inner part of a roll of cloth to make it weigh heavier. They told him that there was a church up the road for his trade with God, and that he'd do better preaching to the common people who needed him. The traders defeated him, not with shouting and by throwing things, but with their stares and frightening silence, the weight of everything that counts in this world behind them.

Grimshaw took their advice and set up his stall outside where he did much better with the noisy common rabble, despite their liking for laughing, cursing and throwing things. Some were hoping to sell beads, shuttles and almanacs to the clothiers, others sought hire as weavers or even as beasts of burden who would carry rolls of cloth on their backs. Mercy Rushworth was there. Following the execution of her husband no-one would take her in as a domestic servant or give her any decent employment and after she had sold her spinning wheel she was reduced to catching leeches and selling them to Jonas Appleyard — he who had once paid her five shillings for the body of her own son. She gathered whinberries off the moor, she scraped dung off the common and took it from door to door in a basket on her back to sell it as fuel, and she hired herself out to carry the weavers' pieces from Haworth to the piece halls, often returning stumbling over the moors with a weft of over a hundredweight. Grimshaw caught her eye and the eye of many others whom he knew to have sunk under their sins to the level of having to beg at the doors of the Piece Hall. He was powerfully moved by God's word and he preached for an hour until all business was concluded within and the members of his temporary congregation were required by their masters.

Grimshaw also went with Maskew and Paul Greenwood to the

127

feast at Luddenden on August 4th. There was no rain to spoil this one — the Methodists had not prayed for it. Early on there was a delicate mist, like a half-transparent membrane protecting the valleys before the sun gave birth to them. It strung itself out and vanished under the sun which grew hotter and hotter as the party, gathering more Methodists on the way, travelled a dozen miles southwards by Oxenhope Cross then over the moors at Nab Hill, Cold Edge, Fill Belly and past the Rocking Stone to reach Luddenden Dean. The first heather was coming into flower; wasps were appearing and large flies were enjoying the heat whilst buzzards circled overhead. Everywhere people were scything their oats, hunting rabbits and hares, or going to the fair. As William came by the familiar trees and boulders of Luddenden Dean, the noise of the feast drowned the clatter of the waterfalls and the stream. They all grew silent in anticipation.

To take his mind off memories, William got his band singing hymns. Thus they burst manfully onto a slope on the opposite side of the stream to the feast. It was now late morning, everything was in full swing and other preachers were there. Abraham Ingham, whom William had met at Darney's Hardibutts meeting when they expected the Millennium, was slowly undressing to reveal his tattoos while preaching his view of salvation and the coming end of the world. Mary Hepton was claiming to be one of the seven trumpeters who according to the Book of Revelation would announce the Second Coming. " 'The first angel sounded, and there followed hail and fire mingled with blood.' That blood is the blood of women! It is our regular blood!" she screamed.

From their own field the Methodists tried to bawl down the games, drums, fiddles, clowns, bargaining, ale-drinking, rival preaching, oxen, goats, poultry and pigs. A clown on a tightrope thumbed his nose at Grimshaw. Children paddled across the stream, thinking that the Methodists were a new entertainment. One or two drunken and near-legless farmers splashed through the water, looking for a fight but as yet not so drunk that they could not size up Grimshaw's muscles, whereupon they tottered sleepily down into the grass, wishing perhaps that they had stayed with Mary Hepton's entertaining heresies. She attracted a much bigger crowd and they could hear her reciting the speech of Zorobabel from the apocryphal Book of Esdras, which "proved" the superior power of women over men: "And if men have gathered together gold and silver and every goodly

128

thing, and see a woman which is comely in favour and beauty, they let all those things go, and gape after her, and have all more desire unto her than unto gold or silver. . . ." Her thin bones almost rattled with her words. Her mad fervour had intensified since neither Darney's seed nor his relic of a looted foreskin had fertilised her womb. The Methodists tried to outshout her. Thereupon a fiddler and clarinettist, with bunches of heather tucked into their hats, outdid everyone by striking up "The Lonsdale Hornpipe". A drummer mocked with an execution roll. Meanwhile a group of young men made a semi-circle to drive a couple of pigs across the stream. "You'd think it was the English and the French armies in battle!" Paul Greenwood said nervously, whilst they tightened their group with Grimshaw at the front and afraid of neither man nor pig. At the last moment most scattered, leaving Grimshaw, Maskew and Greenwood. But the men, as soon as they crossed the stream, lay in the grass laughing at the rout.

Grimshaw could not keep his eyes averted from the church tower. Whilst Maskew and Greenwood ate in the house of a local Methodist, William went alone to the churchyard. "I shall love you until I die and ever afterwards," he had said to Sarah; and "Until death is a big enough promise for me," she had answered. By God, he would keep his promise. After a few moments staring at her blank dumb grave, he sat a few yards away where sunlight fell on the bank of the stream. He took off his collar and gown because of the heat, whilst he lay back weary and relaxed like an animal moulding a lair out of the grass. His old sense of beauty flooded over him, dreamy and passionate. He was staring up into a deep pool of blue encircled by tree tops so heavy, sleepy and weighed down with leaves, now turned to their leathery mid-summer green, that it seemed they could not possibly hold more. Grimshaw looked sideways, where flies hung like gold dust above the peaty brown stream and then darted away in yellow streaks of light. He watched a vole come out to nibble its paws, and a trout rising.

He suddenly felt Sarah near to him. He knew he would not physically see her, even if he turned, and yet she was more real than a physical presence. She was more real than he had ever experienced her during earthly life. He felt a tension, a tingling vitality in his bones and a sense of reality to such pitch as he had never experienced before. The exquisitely beautiful grass, stones, trees and church were merely shadows of the reality of the ghostly Sarah. She brought a sense of peace. He had come here expecting to be mournful — not to find Sarah and a joy and an amazingly intensified beauty! From a farm up the hillside a dog began to bark, regularly as if it would never stop, and he felt certain that it was animated by Sarah's spirit as also were the leaves shifting softly in the trees and the dust speckled light. All his senses were alert. Then the vision began to fade. The dog lost energy, as if confirming that Sarah's spirit was returning to the shades. The beauty and sense of a new reality slipped out of William's grasp. Disappointed to be left with a world of mere appearances, of colours and forms, without thinking what he was doing he put out his hands and tried desperately to invoke Sarah with a motion of his fingers as if he was tickling trout in a stream. But Sarah was vanishing. He still felt her presence, but no more strongly than when one imagines someone. He could imagine her dress, walk, laughter, and expression but this was not real as were those moments when her whole essence was around him.

Mercy Rushworth was coming slowly downstream, picking her way with her bare legs in the water, her dress lifted and tucked under her belt, a large white cap tied over her head to protect her from the sun. Slung from her neck was a small wooden barrel with a hole at the top through which she popped her leeches. She looked tired. How old was she? She looked seventy but must have been much younger. She stopped absolutely still for a moment and stared into the water. Then she lifted her leg and pulled a leech off it. Grimshaw could see the red sores where they had sucked at her flesh. She realised that Grimshaw was staring at her. The blood flushed her cheeks and he knew that her heart was beating faster. He was full of benevolence, whilst she was as still as an animal that senses an enemy and is concentrating with its life dependent upon its next move. After a moment she took hold of herself and carried on downstream, trying not to hurry but walking clumsily and tensely through the stream nevertheless. She meant to show no unusual emotion, but as she spoke each syllable dropped like a stone from her teeth and her smile came out frightening and murderous. "It's a nice day for sitting in the sun, Parson! — if you've the time to spend."

"Wouldn't you enjoy the promise of Eternity in which the sun of Christ shines always like this, flowers preserve their scents, youth also is ever blossoming and men do not hurt one another, because all who are evil have been consumed in Hell?" Grimshaw asked her.

130

"And my husband at my side?" Oh, how Mercy *did* long for such a paradise! Sometimes — when she smelled the heather or when she recalled moments of her girlhood — the thought of paradise almost made her swoon, and often too it nearly brought her to church again.

"We live in a world of pain and bitterness. I know loss myself," Grimshaw said.

"I think that Heaven should be exactly like Yorkshire is today," Mercy responded dreamily. "Yet when I am in my senses I do not believe a flower should last for ever, for then it would cease to be a flower. In any case, we have our memories."

Grimshaw thought always of permanence — churches of stone, Bibles that preserved the eternal words, souls plucked for ever from burning — and Mercy's reverence for the ephemeral seemed like the ravings of a poor half-witted woman who was beyond redemption. With sadness for one who would certainly be snuffed out in the flames, he watched her hurry downstream towards the fair where she hoped to sell her leeches, a little water slopping out of the top of her barrel. Before she went out of sight, she turned. Tears wetted her face, and she howled, "You damned hard-hearted rascal, you could have saved him if you'd wanted to!"

Grimshaw had other enemies, some of whom belonged to his own profession. When he went to towns where he was not known, the innkeepers, who expected any crowd to come and spend their money with them, complained that Grimshaw preached damnation for more than two hours, that he "upset both pleasure and trade" and that he had a parish of his own to attend to. One of his worst enemies was the Reverend George White of Colne, a town nine miles from Haworth. White was a lapsed Catholic turned Anglican. He had abandoned Jesuitical stringency for its opposite extreme of energetic debauchery. He was a bachelor and his family was in Durham, so he had no-one to whom he must account for himself. His face was pumped full of blood red like a sunset, speckled with pimples that rose up on a tide like a turkey-cock's flush when he got hot with his opinions — which were so strong and simple that he easily over-rode subtle arguments.

In July the sunny weather tempted him to make a tour of the midsummer saints' days in Lancashire. He meant to stay away only for a few days and he left a notice on his church door saying that there would be no service this Sunday. But he had such fun "riding the stang" in Rochdale that he could not bear to leave before the following week when the same group of lads promised to gore a tethered bull. It was White himself whom they mounted on the stang, the piece of wood that they carried across their shoulders. An old pan which he beat with a stick was around his neck, and when they went to bait a woman who was said to bully her husband, White chanted louder than anyone:

> "With a ran tan tan
> On my old tin can,
> Mrs Holmes and her good man!
> She banged him and she banged him
> For spending a penny when he was in need. . . "

The scowling scolding woman reminded him of his Colne parishioners. From that night onward he found it impossible to return to them and he gave himself up to whatever company he met, letting them pass him, drunk and helpless as a baby, from town to town.

When White got back to Colne late one Saturday evening he found twenty bodies waiting to be buried. No-one had known his whereabouts or when his return would be, and the whole town was frightened of the rotting bodies causing a plague. (They could not appeal to the magistrate because White himself held that office.) His church was full of people who had been suffering sleepless days and nights whilst waiting for the funerals. As soon as it was known that the reverend was coming down the street (too drunk and angry to notice the scowls around him) the clerk hurried to warn him. As White came through the churchyard — almost falling into the holes dug ready for coffins — he saw at the west door the churchwardens holding back the people in the nave, some of whom in their misery and anger would have murdered him.

To frustrate their revenge White went brusquely to the base of the tower where the coffins were collected and at eleven that evening he began his funeral sermons. His wig was awry and he had to keep grasping the wall or the edges of coffins. Once he went out to be sick, which helped him considerably. As he gradually sobered there came a weariness and a realisation of the task before him. He felt like a man looking over a vast field which he must plough. He was as insensible to the soft weepings and mutterings in the church as a farmer is to the misery of cattle in a market. After each run-through of the burial formula, the coffins were carried into the graveyard. Occasionally White looked into the eyes of old people who had lost their partners and who were wondering why they had been brought into this world to suffer, or into the faces of parents who had lost their children and he flinched, because he did not really have an unkind heart. Just before dawn, the clerk went round the church to replace the guttering rush-lights. The morning light came in at the open door with a soft grey-yellow reflection of shorn fields and mown grass that spread its colour upon the nave walls. The sun rose boldly, bursting glittering like coloured dew through what was left of the stained glass broken in the windows, and birds' song mingled with the sound of spades.

White would have slept through this Sunday morning, but on his way home the clerk told him that the Methodists were going to preach in his churchyard, just as they had during each Sunday of his absence. A man named William Darney was in town. "Those damned Methodist rascally pedlars should be in gaol — and will be, too, for this impertinence!" White threatened. Instead of going to sleep he had his housekeeper serve him breakfast, then he walked up and down cursing the Methodists whilst the housekeeper, a simpleton glad not to be in the hospital, stared at him.

When White reached his church, Darney was preaching by the north wall, to which un-sacred part the wardens had driven him. His badly-fitting wig kept slipping sideways, mud was splattered on his new clothes and the recently shaven part of his face had turned red and sore with the sun. White's congregation within consisted not of the poor folk who had been awake all night (though some of these were now listening to Darney) but of respectable townspeople who had come to find out what excuses he might give for his escapades. "Are we to allow rude pedlars to preach to us — who give us superstition for religion and who, having no qualifications, make for the decay of learning?" White demanded, looking steadily at the merchants. "Pedlars who upset the realm, ruin trade and spoil the innocent and wholesome traditional amusements of the people. I will use all my power as a magistrate and minister to see honest industry flourish!" The day ended with Darney fastened to the whipping post as "a very disorderly person wandering about giving no good account of himself and disturbing Divine Service".

John Wesley returned to the West Riding on August 22nd, speaking at Halifax Cross, Bradford, and Keighley. Many of the Halifax Society advised him not to preach there as crowds were waiting to attack him. But Wesley relished the danger and fight. Although they were "roaring like the waves of the sea" (as he wrote in his diary) he quietened most of them with his speech. Then a rich clothier began to scatter money amongst them to "shout up in support of Church and King". This broke up Wesley's meeting and he moved off with a group of twenty devout followers to hold a more sedate prayer session in a tenter field. Wesley survived similar rowdy meetings until he reached Haworth. There he preached at five in the afternoon, after Grimshaw had led the prayers. It seemed that everybody in the district felt the importance of hearing Wesley, Grimshaw and friends — as if they all knew that there was the spirit of a new age in the air. The church was so full that people brought ladders and chairs from which to peer through windows. A large group — the entourage that had attached itself to Wesley in the previous towns — followed him up to Sowdens and were accommodated for the night. Grimshaw gave up his bedroom to Wesley whilst he himself slept with Maskew and a few others in the barn loft. At four o'clock next morning Grimshaw was up and singing hymns to himself whilst he cleaned John Wesley's boots. He polished every part with devotion and was pleased that Wesley took no more notice than if the task had been performed by a servant. At five o'clock John Wesley, after leading family prayers at Sowdens, preached again in the parish church to almost as many people as on the previous evening.

At mid-morning Wesley and Grimshaw at the head of their band went to Colne. All the way through Haworth and Stanbury, men took off their hats and women curtsied. Several also grasped the horses' heads and begged the preachers not to go on, saying that the "Colne mob" would kill them. The heroes paused to rest their horses at the parish boundary on the moors, where around them the hills had been ground and ground again into smooth outlines by the weather. Grimshaw waved his podgy hand over the landscape, like a sower casting seeds. "When I first came to this country, if I had gone a whole day's journey I could not have met with one truly serious person. But see now how God has blessed the poor services of his minister," he said with the satisfaction of one certain that

Methodism was responsible for taming the barbarians hidden in their black cottages, for the hay and oats in the valleys, the oxen by the stream, the clothiers' smart houses surrounded by fields full of tenters, and the enclosures on the moor fringes.

As they descended the valleys, through Wycoller, Colne and on to Roughlee, they were given more warnings. But Roughlee seemed deceptively peaceful. Oats were provided for their horses which were put to graze in the sunshine on Pendle Hill. In the farmhouse kitchen where they preached, shutters were closed against troublemakers and rush-lights burned. Wesley examined the Society's accounts, making sure that there was an entry for the rum to be consumed later by the preachers. Chairs were found for the principal Methodists whilst everyone else stood in a tight-packed crowd, some even being forced into the larder. Men and women tried to keep to separate sides of the room but it was difficult in so crowded a space and several found themselves embarrassingly surrounded by the opposite sex. Maskew began the proceedings, speaking on our need to prepare for death — this last week he had heard that his father had been executed for poaching. He was nervous but he affected a rock-like composure; he disliked having faces close to him and he continually shifted his glance to the ceiling or to the back of the room. Grimshaw studied his disciple's performance, beaming with uncritical pleasure at it. Wesley was more conscious of Maskew's unlettered style. "He has faults of superfluity of imagery and personification, acquired from the vocabulary of the ignorant and vulgar with whom he has generally conversed," he said to Grimshaw, loudly enough for Maskew to overhear.

Maskew had preached for a quarter of an hour only when there were sounds of people gathering outside, the more frightening because the Methodists, shut in their room, could see nothing of the enemy. Maskew hesitated, and then blushed at having shown cowardice. In a few moments there came a banging on the shutters which stopped him again. Wesley impatiently tapped his fingers on his chair — he was itching to take over the assembly himself — whilst Grimshaw and others of the most bulky men moved to place their backs against shutters and doors, and grasped their sticks tightly. After one pregnant silence outside, they all heard footsteps on the roof. But before the worshippers could douse their fire, a slate was placed over the chimney and smoke poured in. A shutter had to be opened and the enemy fought their way into the room.

135

Meanwhile in the Square, George White — accompanied by a boy with a drum and two men with a barrel of ale — set himself on the steps of the market cross. After an audience had been drummed up, he proclaimed, "Notice is hereby given that whosoever is mindful to enlist in the King's service under the command of the Reverend Mr White, Commander in Chief of His Majesty's forces, for the defence of the Church of England and support of the manufactory about Colne, both of which are now in danger, he shall receive first a pint of ale advance and other proper encouragement!" People came hurrying with their tankards held eager for the beer before it ran out, and within an hour twenty men were enlisted. George White's army — banners flying, drums beating and bugles sounding; armed with stones and sticks, giving out blood-curdling cries — reached the farmhouse as a gang of women, with paints and dyes and shrieking with laughter, tore the clothes off Maskew and daubed him. Four men hauled him away to the river and swung him backwards and forwards. It felt as if the flesh was shrinking on his bones. He decided to trust entirely to the Lord and instantly he was completely at peace, even though helpless in the men's hands. The next moment he was sailing through the air, he felt the shock of cold water, then his head hit a stone and he was senseless. Meanwhile White, who was unable to bring himself to punch colleagues of the cloth, demanded that Wesley and Grimshaw go with him to the Constable at Barrowford. The army expected Wesley to refuse and to fight over it, but when the preachers mildly agreed to go, one of the frustrated "soldiers" punched Wesley and another threw a stone at him.

The Constable sat with a bottle of brandy at the inn. He refused entry to the rabble, so White angrily drew up his troops outside, marching up and down before his lines of shopkeepers, weavers and tradesmen, loudly trying to impress with the martial spirit of his soldiers.

"Mr White wishes you to undertake to stay away from his parish," the Constable said to his prisoners.

"Mr White is almost permanently absent himself, raking about in London or up and down the country, expecting his parishioners to pray for him whilst he enjoys free board and lodging in York prison!" Grimshaw responded.

Grimshaw and Wesley (dabbing at cuts on their faces) argued with the Constable for an hour, by which time Maskew had been fished out of the river with a clothes-prop. When he had been revived, a coat was thrown over him and he was dragged and carried to the inn. White impatiently grabbed Maskew by the ear and hauled him like a naughty schoolboy into the Constable's presence. Maskew was dripping with mud and paint, the taste of blood filled his mouth and his eyes were almost closed.

"Do you not have men who know only the plough preaching for you?" the Constable asked Grimshaw.

"A plough, sir, may make as good a priest as a popish academy! Should you think it a disgrace to follow a lay preacher who is also a ploughman, remember that Elisha was ploughing when called to succeed Elijah! Men have through all times discovered faith without the aid of learning — in my own parish I could produce several hundred besides Mr Maskew."

"Then is every bold visionary to set himself up as a guide?" the Constable asked, smiling.

"In parishes such as this where he, that should be, is no leader," Wesley answered.

"The consequence is that daily work and family life are neglected when people are running off to Methodist meetings all the weekdays!" White shouted.

"Trade receives more obstruction in one week from those who go a-hunting, or who allow themselves three hours' idleness in what is vulgarly called a 'noonday sit', or loiter away precious time in drunkenness in your town on market days, than from all those who give themselves to this new form of worship in three months!" Grimshaw said.

"Will you stay away from my parish or will you not?" White demanded.

"I would as soon cut off my hand as make such a promise!" Grimshaw said. "And all of our preachers are ready to go to prison or death for Christ's sake!"

"These are a tumultuous and raging people," the Constable remarked, surveying Maskew's condition. The Constable was weary of the business. He declared that the Methodists had suffered enough, dismissed them and advised them to obtain dissenting preacher's licences before returning again to Colne.

White was furious at this mild judgement. He got against the window, so that they could hear him outside, stamped his foot and shouted, "I vow to God that before these Methodists preach in my parish I'll sacrifice my last drop of blood to root them out!"

As Wesley opened the door the unsatisfied crowd forced him back. The same happened to Grimshaw when he left by the other exit. The Constable now washed his hands of the whole matter, whereupon Grimshaw put his head down and ran at the men blocking his way, turning sideways at the last moment to ram his shoulders at them. Wesley more dandily followed. Both preachers were kicked, rolled in the mud and tossed from person to person in the crowd which shouted "God save the King and the devil take the preachers!" Grimshaw enjoyed the fight, unequal as it was. "Get out o't'way wi' thy spindle shanks and let them kick me, Mr Wesley!" he shouted. The only thing that unnerved him was that his wig was torn from his head and he was embarrassed by his baldness.

Chapter 10

JANE GRIMSHAW DIED at Kingswood School when she was thirteen years old — two years after she went there. All the children were exhausted from rising at four a.m. and being continually at work until they returned to their beds at eight in the evening. During the winter there was a smallpox epidemic from which the children tended not to recover because they did not wish to — on the contrary, they courted death with ecstasy, its image being mixed with that of God. Death was God's country and a dead body was the door to it.

As the epidemic took its grip, groups of pupils were taken through the frost-bound forest to see the body of an old lady wrapped in her winding sheet and waiting to be carried into her alabaster mausoleum. Her features were relaxed into an image of bliss, yellow-white like softened wax. The great mausoleum, of colourless alabaster except for a few faint pink streaks, like flesh that has been drained of blood, was designed in the form of a four-poster bed with a carved canopy and curtain: Death's bridal-bed. The surrounding stone angels had pouting fleshy lips, rolling eyes and half-rising, half-falling postures, expressing the orgasms of brides. The mausoleum almost filled a room especially built for it on the side of the parish church chancel. Whilst the children blew on their hands, tried to noiselessly stamp their feet and mingled grey balloons of sickly breath in the unheated church, the schoolmaster preached.

It was the sump of the year. In the forest, trees and bracken seemed frozen into blackened rock draped with a lace of frost. As the pupils marched back to school in their rigid order, groups of miners were singing wassail songs. They were already drunk from the gifts given them to buy fertility for the new year, and carried elder boughs and wooden bowls, decorated with holly and ivy, which they rattled impudently at the Methodists. At one group of huts there was no wassailing. The children knew that behind drawn curtains were the bodies of miners killed in a pit accident. Here stones were thrown at the children.

139

Back at the school, sickness, sanctity and rebellion smouldered. After chapel groups of eleven-year-olds stayed up all night, weeping and "wrestling with God" until even the master who had encouraged them panicked because he had released a force that he could not control. Fearing that they might injure themselves, he sent for the maids. But they too were "caught up". Everyone longed for the bliss that had overcome the few who were touched by an invisible spirit and cried, "I'm saved, I'm saved!" These the teachers were able to persuade into the dormitories where they conducted hysterical services (being the children of preachers). This continued until four in the morning, the time to rise. Everyone was hoarse. A maid who was perfectly healthy swooned upon the chapel floor and said happily that she was about to die. Children mobbed the teachers, telling them how much they wished to "flee from the wrath to come" and begging to know what to do to be saved. Even the youngest at least refused to eat for the day. Groups spent their time in corners until the prayers for Grace to descend passed inevitably into funeral services.

John Grimshaw decided to keep clear of all this. He avoided meetings and arguments lest his resolve weaken. (As he lay isolated in bed, the prowling schoolmaster suspected him of masturbating and slyly watched for tell-tale movements of the covers.) Jane however — unknown to her brother because they were in separate buildings — soon collapsed with sickness. As she lay sweating in her cold dormitory, which was noisy with coughing, grey and misty with breath and twilit through the short days at the end of December, she heard the colliers singing "Jolly Old Hawk" outside the school:

> "Jolly old hawk with his wings so grey,
> Send to my love on the twelfth-most day. . . ."

— each verse a different spell to drive away the demons that haunted the world after Christmas. Despite Jane's longing for Heaven, she wanted also to stay and enjoy the spring. She remembered pace-egging in Yorkshire and the mummers, wearing animal skins, with antlers on their heads. She had been told that these were diabolical things and yet even though she was on the brink of Heaven or Hell she could not keep herself from thinking of them. The child tried to fling her thoughts out of her mind but she could not forget that warm, rich life. Often Jane woke from her sickly sleeps with a smell in her nostrils of the Yorkshire moorland when the grass was burnt in

140

April. One night in the dormitory she remembered her father singing heartily and happily around Sowdens, "Praise God from whom all blessings flow". She awoke once to the pure perfume of heather. On another night she saw Heaven; it was airy moorland paved in gold and the heather was in flower. The angels were dressed in silver, their robes deliciously flowing. She told the schoolmistress about her vision and everyone gathered around her bed as if she were a prophet, and in awe of her. Just before her death, in the middle of January when the frozen forest was black and hard as enamel, a hymn trickled from her lips. It was like the thin autumnal song of a robin. Soon her light flesh and bones were buried in Bristol, without her father or anyone else of her family except John Grimshaw knowing anything about it.

Jane's father was busy at York bringing before the Archdeacon's Court nine young men for "leaping, jumping and practising disorderly exercises on the Lord's Day and thereby neglecting to attend Divine Service". It was three weeks before Grimshaw got to Bristol. After he heard about her, his "little Jenny" haunted his reflections no matter what he turned his mind to; her fleeting similarities to her mother, which had so often dazzled him; the fair hair, the poetic temperament that loved flowers. His only comfort was that she had died the death of the righteous — which was more than would ever be said of his intractable son. The boy had been twelve when William brought him here. Now at fourteen he was a foot taller and the same height as his father, with awkward limbs that had grown too quickly, a breaking voice and the shadow of soft, dark hairs on his cheeks, and a manner faltering awkwardly between aggressive bravado and introspection. He had a habit of climbing high trees where no-one dared reach him and staying there all day with a slice of bread, a bag of apples, a flask of ale and a profane book. One of the volumes he got hold of was entitled *Curious Habits of the East, by a Seafaring Gentleman*. Another was *Marriage amongst the Indians*. When John went into the forest he felt as though his eyes were at last opening — it was as if school had doused him in grey ashes that could only be blown away by forest breezes. But nobody understood why he climbed trees and was so insensible to his eternal fate. He had hardly opened his *Christian Perfection* or his *Life of Mr Haliburton*. Sometimes he even got drunk with the colliers — when he was not fighting them. (There were often battles. When, for instance, the miners armed themselves with scythes and hay-forks to attack the new

141

turnpikes, the Kingswood boys broke out of school to defend them. Worst of all, Grimshaw was informed that his son played with himself in reckless defiance of insanity, impotence, blindness and the hair that would grow on his palms.

The boy was now tall enough to look his father straight in the eye as he told him that he would not stay for another day at Kingswood School. He longed to return to Yorkshire, but he said that if he was left behind he would board a ship from Bristol to the West Indies and return to Haworth at the age of twenty-one to collect his inheritance. He looked very determined when he spoke of his fortune, for he knew he could not be deprived of Lockwood's money, and he would now receive his sister's share also. The next day Grimshaw decisively told John that he would apprentice him as a weaver to John Greenwood: thus he would at least learn the trade that was buttering his bread. They went back to Yorkshire together, taking a bundle of Jane's sad little effects: a few tiny clothes, fragile as dead butterflies, and her mother's chap-book of pressed flowers which Jane had kept with her Bible at her bedside to remind her of home. Father and son realised that there was little contact between them. John saw that he was the rich son of a poor father. The Haworth perpetual curate looked like a shabby tradesman. He had turned forty, he complained about his arthritis which was the penalty of "itinerating" in all kinds of weather, and he self-consciously fished out of his pocket a pair of spectacles, saying that they were the gift of Mr Wesley. John could not understand why his father wanted to be humble. The Grimshaw family crawled on the earth when they could have lived in splendour at Ewood, which was now gathering dust behind its shutters.

But John could not be drawn into expressing an opinion on this or any other subject — he merely answered "I don't know," or "I can't remember". He did not care about his father's worries — Darney's continuing "raillery" or the way that the Yorkshire Methodists were being "stolen" by the Baptists — and his whole interest seemed to be in the passing landscape. He behaved as if he was worn out and from time to time William took a surreptitious look at the palms of his son's hands, whilst John observed how restlessly his father sat upon the seat, as if his bowels were painful, letting out foul smells. John brightened only when they saw the first Yorkshire hills. But as they came up the steep hill from Keighley — in John Greenwood's vehicle, which had come to meet the stage-coach — the boy's home town of which he had dreamed, boasted and expected so much, drowned him in a nauseous disappointment. It looked more or less the same: the long steep street, the church at the top, the women gathered at the wells, the woolcombers working in their basements, and the manure heaps. But it lacked the cheerfulness that he'd imagined, and his father wore there a pompous pride which the boy could not stand. William Grimshaw talked about Haworth as the most sinfully wicked spot in this especially wicked county of a wicked country, yet it seemed to John that everyone had become more Methodistical than ever — even Jonas Appleyard, when his father called at the apothecary's for some powders for which he wouldn't explain the use, and Molly Shackleton. What was the point of being a rich young buck in such a town? Methodism had killed his mother, his stepmother and his sister.

John had not remembered the Sowdens rooms, doors and windows as being so small. He had forgotten the smell of blood puddings and oatcakes, particularly strong when Molly kissed him. He watched his father put his sister's clothes in a chest, together with those of his mother and of his stepmother which Molly had not worn — William Grimshaw was forming a large sad collection of dead females' clothes and they rustled like a disturbed overgrown wood under his touch. John went to sit on the benches in the porch, but that place of massive stones, like the view across the valley, also seemed to have grown more cramped.

For two months John fretted in the Sowdens atmosphere, waiting for his apprenticeship indentures. After a week, when he had remade his acquaintanceship with Thomas Pighells, he was quarrelling with everyone at home and Maskew became so upset that he planned to leave. John noticed that his father brushed more than accidentally against Molly in the evenings when she was wearing his stepmother's silks, and against other ladies, and in a quarrel one evening he dared to say so. He was cruel as only adolescent sons can be to their fathers. How could John understand his father's ache when he saw here a woman with Sarah's long waist, there one with the same slope of shoulders, another with the same breasts and leg? That ache to touch and be touched was also beginning to be felt by John, but the boy had all possibilities before him, whilst his father was sentenced; and the lust that seems admirable in a boy appears repulsive in an old man.

William began to think that the rows with his son were the

fulfilment of those prophecies uttered by his sister-in-law Mary Lockwood on that apocalyptic night of storm when John was born. The boy was growing up with a liking for people with wild hospitable natures, and usually living in large houses. His father took it for the beginning of a decline into drunkenness and debauchery, but to John, the generous hearts of his friends seemed closer to God than Methodist parsimony. Their jokes seemed more sensitive than sermons were to human nature. Their laughter made life more bearable than did promises of "eternal life". When he walked into the Pighells' home and saw the huge laughing form of Thomas Pighells, it was to John Grimshaw as if he'd walked into a sunrise. Meanwhile, an escape to the Greenwoods at Ponden Hall was at least *something*, John thought. As he grew up under a not very demanding apprenticeship, since he was never going to need to earn a living by weaving, he almost disowned his father. "I'm not like him," he would say.

William began to tour the village with a horse-whip whilst the psalm was being sung before the commencement of his sermon. His favourite psalm was number 119, because it was the longest. Mad Grimshaw began all his preaching in a fury in which there seemed to be something of an unappeased Viking spirit. "God has a controversy with this nation! The Lord, I am bold to tell you, will shortly pour out the phial of his wrath upon this guilty land!" he told his flock of timid restless sheepish villagers whom he had whipped together. The war that he expected did indeed come in May 1756; it was the Seven Years' War with Spain, a plague upon England for its sins — amongst which Grimshaw included whistling, singing and joking. He preached that the only way to "turn aside God's wrath" was to desist from these sins and also to reprove one's neighbours for them. To fail to do this was as bad as committing the sin oneself and would as certainly send one to Hell. And what a Hell! The furnace was in view of Heaven for the torment to be increased by seeing the angels' delight, and also for the happiness of the chosen to be intensified by sight of their neighbours', friends' and relatives' suffering.

The people of Haworth, trained now to spy upon one another, saw that Grimshaw was already tormented here on earth. He was afflicted with nightmares which he struggled to shake off during his meditation between four and five o'clock in the morning. But all day

144

his unconscious self prowled through the cage of his flesh, bones and clerical cloth. He who had once been a cheerful, idle, optimistic and open-minded, card-playing sportsman, was now industrious and pessimistic. The outward forms of his obsessions were his black clothes and his whip, his home where they dined off wooden plates and stood upon bare stone floors like weavers; but inside him a bleeding chasm was tearing Grimshaw apart. It bled and bled, draining as it were away into his unconscious. Everyone put down his haggard look, his arthritis and bowel trouble to the rigours of evangelism. Only Molly, deep and unspoken within her, knew that he was torn by the battle within himself. As she heard the creaking of the bed where the big man rolled about, the words of his covenant with God running stimulatingly through his head, she knew that evil thoughts gave him no rest and almost drowned him. He would be triggered into unnaturalness after brushing against a lady's dress. Later, whilst Molly tried to turn her eyes from the bed linen, he rushed to his diary. "A dreadful day! Was sorely tempted and sorely gave way!"

His spiritual devotions were the essence of isolation and self-punishment. Yet he drove everyone towards imitating him, until finally the only thing alive for him would be his sacred formulas, clicking like the dry bones of a superstitious relic, mere tokens of departed life; and the pious objects of the Sowdens household — black cassock, black Bible, white candle, glittering brass. At this time the Wesley brothers chose Grimshaw to succeed them as leader of national Methodism, so he was occupied with practical affairs. Recognising that evangelism as well as trade was served by turnpike roads, in 1755 he invested one hundred pounds in the new road to Colne, a share large enough to make him a trustee. John Greenwood paid in one hundred and twenty pounds. When William found himself at the trustees' meeting in the company of the most worldly men of Haworth, including Thomas Pighells, it struck him that material improvements further God's work also.

Both were increasing in Haworth. Grimshaw himself had enclosed a fair piece of moorland between Sowdens and the quarry on the sky-line — to provide grazing for the horses of visiting preachers, he told his sceptical congregation — and now he set about tapping his neighbours' prosperity to rebuild the church. There were enough pious workmen around to do this work quickly, and in one summer the roof and north wall were removed to extend the width, length and height of the building, a three-sided gallery was built and the tower was raised three feet. It was an example of what could be achieved in a material sense by the adoption of Methodist habits — devotion to the job in hand without wasting time whistling, singing and dancing, or abandoning it for the hayfields when the weather was fine. Grimshaw continued to preach amongst the scaffolding, whilst around him grew a building in the latest style — such clean elegant lines that to most of his parishioners it did not look like a church at all; particularly shocking was the removal of the gargoyles and other carvings.

A wave of prosperity had come like the unexpected warm breath of God to the weavers. Everyone was building and all the West Riding was in a turmoil of progress. A dozen clothiers were erecting more splendid houses for themselves. At Heptonstall Robert Greenwood had fought his way out of bankruptcy and used Methodist funds to build a chapel which was also a woollen manufactory during the day. With this system he was able to call on Methodist workmen whom he and other employers were finding, as Grimshaw expected, to be especially reliable with their work, not neglecting it for other inclinations. Although poor people were coming into the West Riding to cultivate the moorland fringes and for the clothing industry, yet even humble artisans and weavers found that they quickly bettered themselves if they led regular lives — profits seemed almost to fall unasked-for into their laps. And they had more time for God who, according to Parson Grimshaw, stood for betterment and regularity. People will always follow a leader who speaks well of what makes them richer, and the visits by evangelists grew into great events. Two or three preachers in turn carried on all day and drew such crowds that despite the enlarged church only a minority could get into it. The "superstitious Papist barbarities" of the old days seemed forgotten — Grimshaw, anxiously looking for signs of the crescent moon being carved upon his shining honey-coloured church, just as they had been on the old air-blackened building, was relieved to find no signs of them. His crowds of visitors grew so huge that he had a wooden platform built outside the window on the east side of the pulpit, so that the preacher could climb through and address the congregations both inside and out. Cataclysmic events — like the great earthquake in Lisbon in 1755, and the war with

146

Spain — attracted hordes of people to join the Methodists in search of some hope and light in the world. Many of them trekked for twenty miles across the moors, and twenty miles back home again.

News of these happenings reached Little Ben Rushworth, who was now eleven years old. Mercy had been forced to put him into a hospital, and was unable to prevent the masters from "apprenticing" him to the owner of a coal-pit in Denholme, near Haworth, when he was six. Mercy was used to seeing agents call to collect gangs of children for labour on the fields or in coal-mines. A waggon came for them, and they left as happily as if they were going on a picnic, although amongst the watching crowd, you could tell who the parents were by their weeping. All the family with whom Ben was lodged worked in the pit. They had once been weavers but the master clothier started drilling in his park and sending his weavers down to look for coal — which they found, unluckily for them. Above ground, the colliers tended to lounge squatting on their heels, smoking clay pipes, and they wore thick white jackets which were scrubbed every week. Below the earth, the father and eldest son hewed whilst the youngsters, boys and girls naked but for large leather belts around their waists, hauled the wheeled tubs that were fastened to them through the tunnelled underworld, the stinking airlessness. The family descended the pit at four in the morning and worked hurriedly because they were paid according to quantity. The father, who was not especially unkind, often beat his naked coal-besmirched daughters and sons, underneath the earth where everything was so different to the world above. When first taken down the pit, Ben like all the children howled with terror, which soon settled into a hopeless snivelling, as it always did. When he fell asleep over his work he was cradled on heaps of coal. His first job was to hold candles for his elders to work by. Then he was set for twelve hours a day alone in cramped little holes behind the trap-doors working the vanes that circulated air through the mine. How especially cruel boredom is to a child! In these vile corners Ben taught himself to read, poring over his grandfather's Bible by the light of candle ends — when the miner could afford to let him have them, for working the traps could be done in darkness and Ben often worked thus for days on end. Turning the vanes with one hand and the pages of his Bible with the other, Ben could ignore his cramp and after a twelve-hour stint he was often almost unwilling to be drawn out of the mine.

147

The miner's wife pulled the children out by turning a winch. Having more youngsters than she wanted, she often carelessly raised them too hurriedly and the infants banged helplessly from side to side of the shaft. This was the most terrifying part of their day because sometimes the rope snapped. They would rather stay in the pit all night than face this terror of perhaps being dropped into it to die at the bottom of the shaft. The woman, with a lot of evil in her for which she could find little outlet, teased the children by calculating how quickly she dare haul. They squealed like rats trapped in a hole and the noise mixed with the rattle of stones and clay falling at some terrifying distance below into water. Then the naked children came like worms out of the earth. The hair was scuffed off their heads by the roof of the mine and by the tubs as they butted them along the passageways; there were horrible pale, sore indentations and scabs around their waists where the belts had been, and their limbs and scalps were running with blood and coal dust. As they came into the light, the woman always cackled the same rhyme:

"Little man in t'coal pit
Goes knock, knock, knock,
And when he's done his work
He peeps out t'top."

Miners — if they survived — grew up with superhuman strength and determination. Ben was short, muscular and pale, with the secretiveness of the colliers — a separate clan. He became known as the boy who could read like a parson; the lad who was never too tired to go roaming the countryside all the few hours he had free. He would have been bullied for his oddities, were it not for his skill in capturing young larks and training them to sing in cages — a hobby of the miners. The mine made Ben sure-footed in the dark and so he was able to travel on foggy starless nights over the moors when others would have been lost. He became well known at inns, burial societies and nonconformists' meetings all over the West Riding.

One evening when Ben was with weavers' apprentices in Heptonstall, William Shent's son John, now a boy of nineteen who had become one of Grimshaw's assistants, was sent by him to preach at the Methodist Society. Robert Greenwood wouldn't let the boy into the preaching house nor let him stay for the night in the preacher's bedroom. "We've been sent nobbut a lad! We shall be ruined!'' Greenwood complained. When the news passed a few doors on to the inn, everyone laughed and repeated plaintively, "We shall be ruined!" — Robert Greenwood having already been ruined by his speculations upon the Millennium. Ben, so serious the remainder of the time, was sillier than anyone else after he'd had a little to drink. The apprentices, with Ben leading them in the darkness, left the inn at midnight, stumbling, singing, shouting "We s'l be ruined!" and tapping on windows up the black, cold street, its stones glittering with sour and gusty autumnal rain. When they got back to the weaving shed where they slept amongst the looms, they found that their master had taken pity on Shent and given him shelter there. Moreover the boy wanted to preach to them before they settled down for the night. Shent, with a gesture imitated from John Wesley, fixed an unwavering eye upon one person — Ben — and, unaware that Ben was the grandson of the man who at his hanging had put the fear of death in him when he himself was a small boy, said "Are you prepared to die?" The other apprentices teased the preacher. They were too good-hearted to harm him and they soon went off to their beds, but Ben stayed watching. "Bring me a rope," John Shent said to the few who were still awake. Standing near the centre of the room where there was a hook in the ceiling, he silently made a noose and climbed onto a chair to tie one end to the ceiling, the loop around his neck. The other apprentices rushed out of their beds. Shent then calmly took off the noose. Thus came the moment when — in a low attic full of the candle-spread shadows of looms and beams, smelling of wefts, stale beer and the sick of drunken apprentices — Ben first heard someone speak with moving enthusiasm about the events at Haworth. He learnt that on the following Sunday, not only Grimshaw but also George Whitefield would be preaching and thousands would be coming from all over Yorkshire.

On that day in the dark, damp and cold several hours before the October dawn, Ben strode across Oxenhope Moor to join the Heptonstall Methodists who were going to Haworth. He travelled so swiftly and quietly through the darkness, without a lamp, that he disturbed neither animals nor people. Yet all over the West Yorkshire moors, roosting hens, unsettled too early by the pilgrims, fluttered noisily as if they were about to explode into feathers up to the barn roofs; goats and cows, impatiently milked, kicked over buckets that

149

rang across the darkness; wedges of light shot through doors or windows and signalled across the moors; boots rang briskly on the stones.

The Heptonstall Methodists gathered secretly on a cliff top at the edge of town to watch for their coming friends. All over the oozing landscape lights slid and jerked downhill until they joined with Darney's and Maskew's parties coming from Todmorden. Voices were raised excitedly despite their fear that the landscape might be full of enemy ambushes. Friends who had not met since the last preaching discussed recipes for baking, cures for the afflictions of humans, poultry and cattle, the prices of cloth at the piece halls and fables of Methodist persecution. As they came flushed and puffing up the scree to those who were waving lanterns on the cliff edge, the dawn was breaking faintly silver and orange — it would surely be a fine day.

By now there was a couple of hundred of them, setting off to skirt Heptonstall and avoid the first inhabitants roused to watch them from tenter crofts at the backs of houses, and chagrined at missing their chance to be abusive. Ever afterwards, the cliff edge where the Methodists met was called "Hell Hole" because of the conversations that were believed to have taken place there.

"I told my husband that I had visited both Heaven and Hell in my sleep, but he would not believe me," a woman named Zillah Feather said. " 'Have you lost your senses?' says he. 'No', says I, 'I have come to them!' I told him I had seen there several that we knew. Elizabeth Grimshaw was in Heaven where she shone like a sunbeam. I saw Amos Sanctuary who cheated my husband over a bag of flour. He was tumbling head over heels into Hell. 'Nonsense,' my man says to me, so I challenged him to go see whether Amos Sanctuary was alive or dead. He found he had been taken ill that night and the next morning he was dead just as I had described, with his head and heels together from the pain, for his soul's unredeemed descent into Hell. 'It's a sin to cheat us over flour,' says I."

"Did your husband not beat you for following us Methodists, and later fall over a cliff?" William Darney asked.

"The Lord does not always give us time to dawdle over our atonement."

"There was a woman down Todmorden used every week to insult preachers on the river bank, and one day when she was doing her washing and wringing out her mop at that same spot, she was sucked in and drowned in a whirlpool. 'I am being sucked into Hell!' she shouted. She knew where she were going, like.''

"Good Mr Grimshaw's successor at Todmorden, he were not one of the Elect, he caught the palsy after he'd preached against the Methodists.''

"They say that on the day Mrs Grimshaw was elected she saw in vision the place where she was to go and the hour of her dying, and that she passed away exactly at that time,'' Zillah said.

"When Elizabeth Grimshaw was dying redeemed I heard her whisper, 'Fret not for I am going to Jesus and to help the angels praise God,' '' Maskew told them.

The eleven-year-old Ben felt left out of this conversation. It seemed to him that they spoke in a special language, like horse-dealers — what *were* "redemption", "conversion", "election" and "atonement"? As the band travelled through the steep woods to reach Hardibutts Farm, the few who noticed the child perceived the pain on his face; he had the expression of a Christian martyr. Sometimes they rested at wayside springs. At one of them Maskew said, "Dusta want to break bread with us, lad?" and Ben grabbed it with the greed of someone who doesn't know where his next meal will come from. Maskew inquired his name. "I'm called Ben Rushworth after my grandfather. He was a hero. Ask anyone i' Haworth!"
"I'm from Haworth myself,'' Maskew said, and asked Ben what had become of his father, whereupon Ben told him that he'd gone to be a soldier fighting the Spaniards.

As they approached Hardibutts Farm, more folk were going about their Sunday business. Those on their way to a genteel service at Heptonstall church turned their noses up at the rabble of besmirched pilgrims and women dragged their children indoors. There were also friendly people. Furtive women, in fear of their husbands, darted out of their cottages to offer food and drink. There was no point in the Methodists being secretive any more and when they saw aggressive groups ahead, they outfaced them by singing hymns. Darney kept in the leadership, shaking his fist and bawling blessings. Ben gripped his Bible, ready to punch someone over the head with it. It was nine o'clock when they reached Hardibutts and the sun was hot on south-facing slopes. With a clatter of sticks they fell in the yard, on the grass, or onto the hay in the barn.

151

The Hardibutts Methodists were a well-disciplined group nowadays — the most rebellious had either departed for America or had joined the Baptists — and a short prayer meeting was held before everyone was given food or they shared out what they had brought with them.

Nearly three hundred now ascended the moors. Several of the gangs who had trailed after them to throw stones had perhaps also been troubled by secret nightmares, for they stuck to the Methodists like burrs to a passing flock of sheep, all the way to Haworth. The closer they got to it, the more crowded the lanes were with other bands, all tired and muddy but keeping their spirits up by singing hymns. Preaching had already started and the churchyard was packed, with others perched on roofs to watch William Grimshaw and George Whitefield on the scaffold. This strange platform, like something built for a parliamentary election, was in itself sufficient to attract crowds of sightseers. Some of these had staked clearings for themselves in the churchyard and were dining on cooked beef, rum and ale. Other groups were singing rival hymns at the back of the crowd. Gypsies and pedlars were selling charms. The inn was full and another group of people was having its accidents attended to at the apothecary's — mostly by Ruth Appleyard whilst Jonas dashed excitedly all over town. The October fair was to start on the following day and the spectacular preaching event was Grimshaw's attempt to usurp the Feast. Pigs, bulls, sheep and poultry were crammed into enclosures and their howling rivalled the Methodists. Farmers and weavers, angry at finding all accommodation taken up, came belligerently to the churchyard.

This October was the fifth month of the war and Mad Grimshaw was shouting, "I will cut off the pride of the Philistines! I will take away his blood out of his mouth and his abominations from between his teeth! . . . I will cut off the chariot from Ephraim and the horse from Jerusalem and the battle bow shall be cut off!" The thousand silent pale faces raised below him were like a field of wheat vulnerable to his scything oratory — unless the crowd was a great monster curled around the church, tense, sighing from time to time. Beyond it could be heard the misery and bewilderment of animals brought to the fair. Out of the packed masses came the quiet crying of women whose men were away at the war. Here and there one crumpled down amongst the muddy feet, her face pressed into her knuckles. There bubbled up at various places the ecstasies of the converted, and Ben

152

Rushworth was one of them. He felt his heart broken to pieces by the oratory; his head turned to water, his eyes became fountains of tears — such metaphors, taught to him by the many preachers whom he had heard, seemed to rise up through the soles of his feet and run through his limbs as he listened, for he had never heard anyone like Grimshaw. He spoke with total calm as if the experience was as common as eating bread, and from time to time allowed himself daring pauses, when the silence of the crowd was tense like a stretched membrane at the point of snapping. The collier child felt an anguish that was beyond description. All around him people were rolling on the ground, clutching themselves as if in pain, shouting "Alleluia!" — some with hysterical joy, others as if it was the whispered last word of their deathbeds; and getting black as pigs in the ground that grew muddier as the day progressed. Eventually the two black-gowned preachers, Grimshaw and Whitefield, retreated through the window into the church, like the two horns of a snail retreating into its shell.

There they administered Holy Communion to as many of the flowing crowds as could get near to them. Ben, although he was not a communicant, joined the queue just so that he could take a close look at the preachers. He formed his strongest impression from their hands that rapidly and fluently passed the cups of wine, refilling them from the flagons that were Grimshaw's gift to the new church. The parson's hands were thick and strong but had grown soft. Whitefield's were finer and their flight was nervous. Ben received another strong impression of Grimshaw's nature from something that happened at the Communion rail. Darney had been making a great fuss in the churchyard, wanting them to sing his own hymns instead of Charles Wesley's; and whilst passing the cup to the kneeling Darney, with the ritual words "Blood that is shed for thee", Grimshaw flicked Darney gently on the ear, winked to the bystanders and joked, "Even for thee, Billy Darney lad!" Ben was then filled with the longing that this Grimshaw who knew how to address all types of people might bring God to the coal-miners.

Meanwhile the business that anticipated the fair continued outside. Unknown to Ben his grandmother was there, partly to hawk what bits and pieces she could, but mainly to find Richard Arkwright who travelled the fairs to buy human hair to make wigs. His sign stood outside the inn: "Rich. Arkwright, Peruke Maker". Arkwright was a twenty-four-year-old barber from Bolton; an opportunist who upset every other barber by offering a shave for one penny, and when his competitors therefore lowered their prices, charging a halfpenny. Though not making any money from halfpenny shaves, he drove the others out of business so that he had a monopoly for the more lucrative branch of wig-making. He had a habit of asking strangers the right kind of questions about their trade and he had thus wheedled a formula for fast dyes out of a village pharmacist who did not know its worth. So in a few years' time Arkwright's tough, fast-dyed, "country" wigs compelled him to travel on his hardy but unpretentious horse all over the north of England, particularly to visit hiring fairs because girls going into service were often forced to cut their hair. Arriving in Haworth, he bargained for a room at the inn. Then he went to the churchyard and stood at the back to study the hair of the girls who were listening to the preachers. Next, whilst customers queued outside his door, he spent an hour in the public room of the inn. This time wasn't wasted. He removed his wig (one well made, but modest, so as not to make him seem prosperous) and sat comfortably drinking with the woolmen, asking them about the new mechanical inventions for spinning and weaving. It was not his business but as he cared neither about the weather, nor politics, nor religion, nor topography, and would not discuss wig-making, it was almost the only subject he *could* talk about in northern inns and through it he had already grasped the principle of Kay's "flying shuttle" and of looms in general. The wool-men told him what he heard everywhere: that the weaving inventions meant there was a great shortage of yarn because hand spinning was not now fast enough. This set Arkwright thinking of how to profit by it.

Meanwhile a queue had formed outside his private room. The longer they'd had to wait, the more ready they'd be to accept a low price. He sat on an upright chair in the centre and boldly faced the door, his knees spread out, his scissors twitching in his right hand and his sack open at his side. He let the girls in one at a time and haggled about a price. Sometimes he met girls meek as sheep who accepted whatever he offered. Others pretended to laugh at the loss of their hair. He never found one who was genuinely cheerful. Some were dragged in by their parents, while others came with their new mistresses who had bargained for the price of the hair in return for training the girl. They all knelt between Richard Arkwright's knees, faced away from him so that he did not see how they felt at the

154

prospect of leaving home for distant houses and farms. But the barber was a connoisseur of the napes of girls' necks and could tell their emotions by the shifting shudders of goose-flesh. He knew misery so well, he might have been a Methodist — although the wig-maker tended to meet the dumb and patient rather than the hysterical variety. Many a woman's most lasting impression of going into service was of the clicking and flashing of plump Mr Arkwright's scissors and of his knees scattered with the hair of girls who had knelt between them — the blonde, the dark, the brunette. Richard loved the feel of all this hair. But he did not scoop it up until his client had left, in order to demonstrate that it was of little value.

Mercy Rushworth came in and knelt between his knees without a word about the price. Arkwright had never seen such a thing before. 'Yours will need a lot of washing,'' he began. She did not answer. She might have been ready to die and he her executioner. ''And then here is — a delicate matter — your age. Woman, you are so grey! I'm afraid that our hair becomes in time hardly worth the trouble of cutting it.'' He did not tell her that he dyed the hair and that coarse-ness was but a small drawback in many of his tough wigs. She still did not answer and his scissors began to click. ''Three pence. Take it or leave it,'' he said. She didn't speak and he started to cut.

Meanwhile the afternoon drew in and the Methodists began to go home, leaving Haworth to the drunken fair-goers. Paul Green-wood's brother William, who had for so many years stayed at Ponden looking after the crops, the animals and his father's business whilst Paul travelled in his adventurous evangelising, could not bear to go home. Since his conversion in the barn on the same Sunday as Paul when Grimshaw had first arrived in Haworth, William Greenwood had followed the faith with the mute unimaginative per-everance of an ox. Now he hung restlessly around Haworth, although he disliked its dreary and despoiled atmosphere — it was like a fair after the cattle and sheep have been taken away — and he wanted neither the inn nor any other company.

At last he resolved that he would go and convert London. He was a man in his thirties, unmarried, overflowing with strength and he set off fearlessly, climbing the southerly hill that walled in his valley. He had never stepped over it before. He did not look back until, sweat-ing, he reached the brow of the hill. The sight of his home broke his heart: the trees and meadows by the stream, the walls of the little enclosures, Haworth town clustered on a hill crest below him, the

155

weavers' cottages scattered up the moor amongst the glitter o springs and falls of clear water. He brushed tears off his face an returned to Ponden Hall, saying nothing about his brief flight.

In the churchyard a vast human manure heap steamed in th sunset. Fortunately the place consisted of flat gravestones from which the filth would be washed away by the rain. Most of ston Haworth was able to withstand the invasion but anything made o wood, such as tenter frames, had been battered. Ben stayed ther until darkness, savouring his memories of the preachers. He had los his companions and he walked alone, in darkness again, direct to Denholme which was only a few miles across Black Moor. The lanes like the churchyard, were trampled into mire. Barns and outhouse as well as cottages were full of Methodists. Ben saw the lamp moving, heard shouting and singing of hymns from crowded barn or lofts. The moorland was seething with lights, as in the morning Because Ben did not carry a lantern, people stared at him as if h might be a felon. At the distant farms, hungry beasts and un-milked cattle, staggering with pain, ran bleating and lowing through the dark pastures to meet the Methodists who had neglected them.

Ben's excitement made him want to stay by himself to savour i and he skirted the groups of people in his path. But eventually the day left him drowned in melancholy. In the churchyard he had fel swept up out of reach of sin and freed, but now to the same extent he was sunk into his fate as a sinner. The excitement around him in the darkness made him think that he alone was without salvation. When he got back to Denholme he could not utter a word to the colliers in the hut. "So we've got a Methodist amongst us, have we?" the woman said after she had wheedled out of him where he had been She whacked him across the ear. "It's not put much of a smile on yer face, has it? I'll not have any 'prentice from here joining all them filthy miserable off-scourings of Yarkshire!"

The day's experience left Jonas Appleyard also feeling like the worst sinner on earth. As a churchwarden he had been invited to Sowdens and during the prayer meeting in the crowded kitchen before Molly Shackleton grumpily served everyone with their meal, Jonas had seen Grimshaw, his eyes moist and his cheeks flushed and bloated with excitement, go down on his knees before Mr Whitefield and say, "I am not worthy to stand in your presence!" What kind of sinner must Jonas Appleyard be then if such a man considered himself to be tainted? All the way home Jonas prayed, prayed, prayed

156

or God's help. Outside his door people who had been injured waited
n pain and Jonas could not face them. He went round to the back
vhere his sister-wife Ruth had lit a fire and was burning blood-
oaked bandages and used poultices. It suddenly struck Jonas that
his was the sign from God for which he had been waiting. He dashed
ndoors, smashed his fiddle and put it on the bonfire.

Chapter 11

GRIMSHAW'S MINISTRY WAS sending out strong ripples in the form of preachers trained by him who combed the villages, farmhouses and clothiers' establishments (generally via their kitchens) of York shire with his message — literally, the written message of Grimshaw's sermons. At first he was very satisfied with his messengers. Barbers, tailors, grocers, farm servants, even the footman of the Countess of Huntingdon, learned to juggle with theology, to fight the Devil and Antinomianism. They dropped from their speech the crude expressions picked up during the practices of their trade and instead imitated Grimshaw's gestures. By copying his mannerisms they put on the mantle of his preaching, and therefore stood confidently before their congregations. They came regularly for instructions to Sowdens; men with little money and poorly dressed who walked all over England, crowded to sleep in Grimshaw's loft and barn, and met in his kitchen (well before dawn on all but summer days) to sing together "Praise God from whom all blessings flow". Molly was sceptical of their enthusiasm and she served them gruffly with oatmeal porridge. Many had come from smoky towns and badly-smelling thoroughfares and they enjoyed the clear water from the spring in the fields and the ringing space of the moors around them. Those who were farm labourers and solitary weavers, on the other hand, and whose dedication made them outcast amongst their neighbours, enjoyed the pious fellowship. Before they departed and left Grimshaw to his loneliness, he was prince of this company — conducting their prayers, correcting their doctrine, every now and then holding a judicious private conversation with one in danger of straying. He told fresh recruits, "If God sends you to preach, all Hell will be up against you, so prepare for the battle — what you achieve must come through the Devil's teeth! You must not expect to gain much of this world's goods by preaching the Gospel. I count every covetous man to be one of the Devil's teeth and he will let nothing go for God but what is forced from him!"

But as his lay preachers reached further and further beyond

Haworth, spreading all over the country, they assumed more and more of Grimshaw's own powers — becoming a threat not only to him but to the whole Methodist Movement's acceptance within the Church. It was not just that they spoke with independent authority. Paul Greenwood had seemed such an amenable young man, but when he got as far away as Norwich, he dared with two other preachers to administer the Sacrament of the Lord's Supper as if he was an ordained member of the Church of England. Such a thing — farm boys acting like ordained gentlemen — could make the whole Movement disreputable and cause it to be associated with Jacobites and Radicals, which was what the leading Methodists feared most. This was a sword which cut Grimshaw's love in two: Methodists would cease being a group within the Church, and instead become a rabble of Dissenters! Already some were seeking to license their meeting places as dissenting preaching houses.

Grimshaw summoned his preachers to Sowdens. He stared at each one in turn to see how he would shift his gaze. "There are traitors amongst us! Well then, if it must be so . . . To your tents, O Israel; it's time for me to shift for myself and disown all connection with the Methodists! How can I justify to my consistory court my preaching in a dissenting meeting house? Not many weeks ago when it was said that I was to speak in such a licensed building, the minister of the parish decided to bring me to court but fortunately as it turned out I preached in a barn nearby and nothing came of it. I tell you I will stay at home and preach in my own parish, or abroad only in such places as are unlicensed!"

Maskew had left before things reached this pass. When John Grimshaw had returned home from Bristol, Maskew had spent as much time as possible away preaching, particularly in the vicinity of Rochdale where he stayed at the farm of the Widow Clegg. It was a stone shack on a moorland plateau, reached by a steep climb up to the rock fringe where one met the wind, or more likely the horizontal rain fleeing in exasperation and terror off the moor. The farm and its tiny enclosure floated like a green raft on a quaking waste of peat, rushes, cotton grass and pools of thick dark water that was like the lees of brown ale. Mrs Clegg's first husband's father had built here: he had been a rush plaiter, a moor-top wanderer who gathered rushes for plaiting into baskets and who lived in temporary shelters made of rushes, stones and petrified tree-trunks. He was as familiar as a curlew with the moorland. The millstone grit of his permanent home, which he had quarried himself, blackened in the air during the twenty years that it took him to erect house and barn. His son wore himself out making a living by plaiting and by occasional work at the quarries, until he had drained some of the moor, manured and sheltered it with enclosure walls. Then the labour killed him. He was such a scrawny creature that it had always been a miracle where he got his strength from and now the neighbours said he had been like the legendary moor-edger's donkey, which "just got used to living without eating when it died". When the weather cleared, the black shacks of these neighbours could be seen scattered at half-mile distances around the moor. Amongst this community, the Cleggs' farm was established as the first Methodist meeting house.

When Maskew married Widow Clegg, John Greenwood gave the couple a loom so that the preacher could earn his sustenance, and Maskew revived his boyhood skill at weaving. He turned their bleak hut into an imitation of his first spiritual home at Sowdens, with prayer meetings at which Grimshaw's letters were faithfully read out. Itinerating Methodists often stayed. In bad weather, Maskew banged away on his loom and on fine days he delighted in working on his own farm. The Widow Clegg (she was still called this long after her second marriage) was, like her first husband, tiny, thin and strong. As she spun, made oatcakes, plucked chickens, spread manure, milked their one cow and helped it with its births, or raised her throat to sing Mr Wesley's hymns, her sinews and muscles worked like the string of their loom. She did everything quickly, running always even when there was no need to hurry, as if it was a habit from trying to keep warm and find shelter from the inclement weather, and she was smilingly exasperated by her husband's slow staring habits. He would absent-mindedly let their cow run past him through the gate whilst he stared across the moor to count a flock of rooks. The mechanical habits of creatures absorbed him — Maskew kept records of the dates when the curlews arrived and departed; and of the weather, comparing snowfalls and the depth of water in the stream year by year. It was the only way he found to articulate the inexpressible. "Yon swallow's fourteen days later than t' first un last year," he'd say, as a means of drawing attention to that joyful creature, turning its russet stomach against the rocks, shining its blue back in a swift glide across the sapped colourless grasses below. In his measuring and counting (a mechanical substitute for joy), he was like a poet who has lost his muse. "Thou'rt a yonderly one!" Widow

160

Clegg said to him, and this was the first time he'd been described lovingly since he was a child.

Despite his happiness, when Maskew scented a "revival" in the air he could not resist leaving home to go itinerating. Perhaps he and many others were drawn to evangelism because they were given excuses for wandering the moors like truant children! His usual companion was Paul Greenwood and these two had a knack of knowing where to go to stir up religion. Having only a few vague reports to work on, they would set off mainly following their intuitions or "trusting to God". Maskew loved that first aroma of the moor as they stepped out — a smell of rushes, peat, sour water and scents from far off brought haphazardly on the breezes. They marched quickly (even though they didn't quite know where they were going) in obedience to Wesley's and Grimshaw's commands to circuit preachers "not to ramble up and down but to go where is needful and there only", although this was a deep frustration of Maskew's dawdling nature. People took them for a pair of artisans travelling in search of work. Eventually they reached the place where they sensed that people were "groaning for God's word" — where it was time to bring into the open everyone's secret fear of being hustled off to an Eternity of fire.

One winter's day the evangelical pair came upon Sawby — a hill-top town like Heptonstall, but on the other side of the Calder Valley, built on an ancient route across the Pennines. The distress here, as potent in the atmosphere as the scent of rotting lilies, was because the local clothiers, grown very rich from trading in Holland, Russia, South America and from speculating in local banking, had enclosed a large area of the common land to make a deer park. They had "improved" the district with a classically-fronted mansion which was as strange upon the moors as if it had dropped from the moon. The surroundings didn't remain moorland for long, because the great family set the dispossessed people to build walls and cultivate a fine turf for the deer. The problem was in what the poor were to do next: they could not all become weavers, despite the volume of foreign trade. In these disturbed times people were driven mad and the Bedlam was full; their screams and rattled chains frighted the new, orderly landscape. Often the villagers vented their frustration on pedlars, tradesmen and wandering preachers.

Maskew and Greenwood gathered their strength at the top of the town and came singing down the centre of the road. Some people

161

skulked away whilst others cursed and threw things. The two preachers ducked and smiled, shouting, "Turn to the Lord and seek salvation!" A woman blushing with surprise and happiness ran towards them from the well and, slopping her jug of water in excitement, hurried them away to her cottage. There her husband left his loom and descended the stairs, his face beaming. He poured out rough ale whilst his wife dashed around Sawby telling her friends, "Mr Grimshaw's preachers is in town!" As usual they came by back ways, separately and secretly. Candles were lit, doors and shutters locked, even though demonstrators were attracted by those same closed shutters. But an amazing thing happened. The woman next door, a secret sympathiser who was only waiting for someone to make her bold enough to bring her belief into the open, knocked on the back of her fireplace as a signal to the woman in the further house, also a secret sympathiser. These two met in the narrow pathway between the rear of their houses and the tenter enclosures, the noises of their husbands' clattering looms drowning their clandestine conversation. They then went off to different parts of the town. And so, by banging on their fireplaces, by word of mouth, by signals across the hills pre-arranged to bring them together, they gathered outside the house that held Maskew and Greenwood. The pair then went to preach in the street which was choked with people who had sad silent faces and queer bubblings of joy in their chests. "Tell us about Mad Grimshaw," they asked, almost holding their breath with awe.

"He is a man who once like you could gain no ground over his lusts and temptations, so life became a burden and he was often tempted to make an end of it. But eventually he trusted entirely to Jesus Christ, till at last he saw the Lord Jesus thrust down his hands and feet from Heaven as if through a ceiling. He knew — as you might know — that he'd be given help and his sins would be forgiven. He has since had a flaming love of the Lord Jesus Christ," Paul Greenwood said.

"The blacksmith up Haworth daren't shoe a stranger's horse on Sunday unless he ask the parson first," Maskew said. Many of the crowd had already fallen to their knees. A huge quarryman shouted, "I'm in the arms of the Lord! I'm saved!"

"They say he had a cow up at Sowdens as followed him everywhere. When he wanted to sell it a farmer asked if it had any faults and Grimshaw answered, 'Not one as you'd have yourself, for she follows me to the pulpit!' " someone shouted, and laughter spread down the street.

"Is it true he begs old shoes off his friends, has them repaired and given to the poor?"

Maskew turned his face to the sky, spread his arms as he'd so often seen Parson Grimshaw do, and shouted fervently, "Supplicate yon yielding throne of Grace and thalt *all* be saved!" For most of the crowd, this seemed to work. An excited carpenter ran through the town like a lunatic shouting, "Sawby's tacken! Sawby's tacken!" Half of the Sawby looms, which had been thundering in sullen undertone to the incessant grumbling, now stopped working. The Lord had come to Sawby in the form of two Yorkshire preachers who entered as humbly as Christ came into Jerusalem! Some people held meetings of their own, in houses, barns, quarries and fields. Preaching went on through the evening until the early hours of the morning. Maskew and Greenwood, who had come for the day, stayed for a week, embarrassed by demands to visit houses and workshops. Men struggled to continue their usual light conversations but there was a brake upon them because their inner fears of Eternity had been brought into the open. As soon as one, a little more silent and obsessed than the others, fell to his knees, all the other workmen tried to out-wail one another with quivering lips and moist eyes.

There were those who could not convince themselves that they had been visited by God's spirit no matter how they called for it. "Does tha not feel a quaking in tha knees?" "Aye, but I've had no breakfast, how else should I feel?" "Hasn't tha palpitations of the heart?" "Aye, a bit, like. I suppose I'm excited." *"That's the speaking of the Lord."* "I dunna think so. It's just me hoping for it." ' "Only give in and then you'll know the descent of Grace, same as the preacher says!" "Give in to what?" *"To the Lord! To the Lord!"* "How can I give in to Him when I don't know what he looks like?" "Eh up! — I can feel it coming! I think it's coming!" "Keep on praying lad, and then thou'lt know it!" "It's gone again." "Keep on! Keep on! Look, pray like me, same as the way Parson Grimshaw does it!" "Has tha seen Grimshaw preaching?" his conversant interrupted, with amazement as if his fellow had visited the King. "I have, lad. I've been over to Haworth to hear him. Now come on, do as I tell thee. Turn thee eyes up to Heaven, like, and press thee knees firmly into th'ground, 'umble like, until Mercy comes." "Lord, it's coming, it's coming, I can feel it!"

There were a few who never gave in, who clung to the edges of the crowd and threw obscenities and other things at the Methodists, but they were soon driven away. Some even took their tools and went to work in another town. Even so they were pursued. "I hear the Lord's up at Sawby?" they were challenged. "When t'preacher told Billy Horsfall he was a sinner, he went home and beat his wife because he thought she'd been talking about him to the Methodists! They're all miserable up Sawby." It was likely that the Lord would grab them whilst they hid from Him. Seized with silence and horror, they trembled and mumbled prayers, afraid to fall to their knees in the present company. "He's got the Sawby plague," people said. It was true. Eventually the man would feel he had to return home.

On the second morning of this extraordinary week, the vicar fled to the clothier's mansion. But the family already knew what was happening, after coming across a party of their servants crouched in prayer behind a hedge, and so carried away as to show no respect for their masters. The clothier was as shocked as the vicar by these barbarous events taking place in the very birthplace of the great Archbishop Tillotson, and they even thought of calling in a detachment of militia.

Another evangelist was John Shent. One day he wandered half-lost across Blackshaw Head, past Bride Stones, and over Black Hameldon, to find the lead miners and the rush plaiters. He crossed a network of peat gullies trickling with water the colour of drying blood: a buzzard's view would be of innumerable branchings like the veins in the face of a weather-beaten old man. This spongy waste was boiling with rain. The world was all mist and wet metallic glitter. Time and again from gullies of sticky wet peat he clambered onto the bristling metallic rushes, or onto the glistening splinters of stone that broke through the moor like bones poking out of the flesh of a hungry cow — these were the hard edges of the moor where the plateau fell away into spectacular valleys, their far sides disappearing upwards into the straggling fleeces of rain clouds. There were great eroded tall black rocks, in some places several rows of them like the nave of a barbaric temple with its roof collapsed. John wandered lost in a great arc until he came upon the miners at the head

164

of Noah Dale. He threw himself without knocking into the largest shack. He was trembling. The woman asked him to take off his soaked clothes, sit on one of her rickety chairs by the peat fire and swallow some broth, but he told her to gather her neighbours together for prayer. She cackled with laughter, spilling broth from her spoon onto the fire. "Most of us hardly ever get down into town, lad, let alone to church. Who'd have us?" She filled a bowl for him although he hadn't asked for it.

"The Methodists will take in all lost sheep," he answered.

She thought that he himself, with his heavy cloak dripping onto the stones and his bedraggled hair, looked like a lost sheep. "Tha seems young to be a preacher. Where are you from?" she asked.

"I am in Mr Grimshaw's circuit in Haworth."

"I'm told he fleights around Haworth with a whip to drive folk to church. Mad Grimshaw should come up here to get my husband out of bed in the mornings, then 'appen we wouldn't have so many mouths to feed. Sit down, lad, and take some broth."

"Will you bring your neighbours?"

"No, lad, I won't. There's no reason for folk up here to think much on God. But dry your clothes and take some vittles afore you go."

Shent then asked the woman for a washing line and she assumed that he was going to dry his clothes. Feeling more at ease herself now that the boy was making himself at home, she brought the line and turned back to her cooking. He tied a noose and put the chair below the hook in the ceiling. When she turned round, he was standing on the chair with the noose around his neck. She ran shrieking into the rain and flew like a scared animal amongst the miners' huts, shouting "Crazy preacher's hanging isself!" and banging in panic on windows and doors. The children ran to where she was pointing. In the doorway they stopped dumbstruck, so the women followed quickly. The chair had collapsed and John Shent, who had merely meant to draw a crowd together with a trick, hung like a wet sack of grain before the fire, water hissing quietly as it dropped from his coat onto the hot hearthstone. To bring them good luck, the children were brought to silently stroke the hands of the warm dead boy, whilst the woman of the house kept the noose intact for ever and used it to bind around her temples to cure her headaches.

Ben Rushworth began to preach in the coal-pit when he was

only twelve years old. He nagged everyone daily until against the dripping coal-face, where it was too dark and wet for tears to be seen, the pitman-weaver who was his master broke down and in gasps admitted his terror of Eternity — that it should go on like this or worse than this, through endless pain, and in life one never knowing which direction one would take in Eternity! "Let us pray," the child said. They put down their tools. The collier's daughter, in the flickering light seeing them fallen in the wet, came crawling as fast as she could. They neither spoke nor moved. She grasped hold of her father's ankle, searching for a pulse, because her terror at her defencelessness if he died was greater than his fear of Eternity.

"Lord I am but a sinful worm in the bowels of the earth," the miner groaned.

"Believe that thy sins will be forgiven and thou'lt be lifted up! Only *believe*!"

Other miners came crawling hurriedly. Ben described to them eternal maimings and explosive fires, so that their fears surfaced and they prayed for the conviction that this life which they suffered was "nobbut a temporary purgatory".

After this Ben's wanderings about the moors turned into purposeful stridings to Methodist meetings, more and more of which were being held in permanent buildings which were not shared with hay and cattle. At the age of sixteen he became a regular preacher. The mood for secession amongst the Methodists had driven some to believe in Calvinistic predestination, some in the coming Millennium and others in adult baptism. Ben visited a Baptists' assembly when Calvinistic farmers, weavers and tradesmen undressed and appeared wearing nothing but loose shifts in front of their neighbours. They descended the stone stairs into the tank, ducked themselves and climbed out, shivering, their hands raised in prayer, their hair streaming — a scene that sent shivers of primitive excitement through Ben so that he wanted to join them. A council of Calvinistic Baptists questioned him for an hour, but the sticking point was his belief in evangelism. They said that as we were predestined for Heaven or Hell there was no point in pedling the gospel like a tinker at a fair; in fact it was a defiance of God's will to persuade people into believing that they could save themselves from Hell if it was intended for them. But Ben would not drop his point of view. He had been born with the physical restlessness of an evangelist and could not abandon his wandering. What he wanted was to tag onto it the theatrical performance of adult baptism. So the council, after deliberating for an hour, sternly told him that he was not one of their number who were bound for Heaven.

Chapter 12

PAIN RAN THROUGH all of Grimshaw's limbs and organs, his sight was weak, and he knew that he would not live much longer. Suffering was concentrated in his bowels. Whether he sat, lay or walked, and no matter how much he prayed to Saint Fiacre, patron saint of those who suffered from piles, his lower organs felt as though they were burning in purgatory. People were already squabbling over his inheritance — an entirely spiritual one, for he had no worldly wealth. The churchwardens and trustees of Haworth were squaring up against the Vicar of Bradford over the choice of his successor, just as had happened before Grimshaw came to Haworth twenty years previously. Methodism was growing powerfully and William was still its leader who travelled all over the North. "By the Grace of God I am resolved never to flag while I can ride, walk, creep or crawl — though I may say, as we do of a drunkard, I live too fast to live long," he said.

Because everyone knew that someone must be chosen to sit on the throne of northern Methodism, it was not as in the old days of warm adventurous companionship. Grimshaw was finding it difficult to talk easily in the villages, as he used to. All but his close followers avoided him because of those awful smells he couldn't help letting out. If they could not dodge him, then in order to cut short his damnations they spoke rapidly about their trivial concerns which bored him and made him shift on and avoid them in the future. The numbers grew of those with whom he avoided direct conversations and it became an embarrassment for him to enter many places. He often seemed too tired to finish his sentences and he would trail off leaving his hearers to guess the drift of his meaning. The only place where speech did not desert him was the pulpit: a tool as natural to him as a boat to sailors, scissors to a barber or a pen to a poet. As always he combated growing weariness by flogging himself into superhuman energy. But he was a man who, though he could address crowds, could not talk to individuals.

And where were William's friends? Maskew was now only a

visitor to Sowdens. Molly stayed but had more sympathy for Mary Hepton and women of her kind than William liked. Paul Greenwood had done the dreadful thing that cut him off from Grimshaw's society. William Darney had been shamed at Conference by Charles Wesley, who read out his doggerel for everyone to laugh at it. John Wesley wanted Darney expelled because of his verse and eventually he was kicked out when it was resolved that "no preacher who will not relinquish his trade of buying and selling, or making and vending, pills, drops, balsams or medicines of any kind, shall be considered as a travelling preacher any longer." ("But observe we do not object to a preacher's having a share in a ship," they added — one of the resolvers having such an investment.)

Grimshaw's other colleague, William Shent, became a "backslider" after the death of his son. He widely admitted that he had been cheating himself by believing in "conversion" and "forgiveness". He realised that he had preached people into going home to destroy the joy and spontaneity of their hearths. If they were slightly uncertain of their faith, they inflicted upon their families countless crises of spirit. At his final meeting Shent knelt before his congregation "groaning for the fulfilment of the great and precious promise of God". He was covered in sweat and his red face already looked boiled in Hell. Nothing else happened. He rose stiffly to his knees. "There is no salvation," he said and walked sternly out of chapel into an extraordinary intoxicated happiness in the sunshine. (This event was mendaciously described in the minutes as "Excommunicated for contumacious neglect of the means of Grace".) He was presumably destined finally for that "hottest place in the lake of fire" which John Wesley reserved for backsliders — for those who had lost faith. But first of all, with relief and then steadily growing pleasure, Shent went into a tavern. The drinkers fell silent and put down their glasses. "There is no God," announced the man who had got his children to pronounce the Father's name as the first word that they spoke.

There was no loneliness like that of a backslider. Having once been one of God's children, nobody else trusted him. It was made worse because he was so extreme in his self-abandonment: he declared that the only way to be free was to sin without conscience. Most of his home district in Leeds was now Methodist and he was deserted by those who had been clients for his doctoring, barbering and tooth-drawing services. His remedies went sour and stinking in

169

their bottles and whilst Shent spent his time sliding downhill to perdition with his drinking companions (amongst whom his practice as a preacher made him a skilled teller of stories) it was his wife and children who suffered most from poverty and the sudden plunge into loneliness.

Grimshaw's son John was becoming more of a rake, neglecting his apprenticeship to spend nights in who-knew-what company at moorland taverns. At the age of twenty-one he possessed Ewood and the Lockwood fortune. The house became noisy with music and burning with lights all night long as John, who inherited a talent for drama, held masquerades satirising the Methodists. He dressed as his father to declaim:

> "We are the sweet selected few,
> The rest of you be damned!
> There's room enough in Hell for you,
> We won't have Heaven crammed!"

When his father remonstrated, John threatened to sell up, leave Yorkshire and open manufactories in Russia.

Many of Grimshaw's earliest converts to Methodism now became "dippers", as he called the Baptists. Their new meeting houses were all over the West Riding, in half-secret places wherever there was water at the backs or ends of villages. Like Methodist societies they mixed prayer with self-help or trade, at their services exchanging vegetables for eggs, arranging for the fetching of wefts or to take pieces to the trading halls. "My chickens are turning into ducks!" Grimshaw roared from preaching platform or pulpit, most unfairly at those who had stayed with him. "They may go into my quarry and dig up as many stones as they can but they shall not have the stones that I have quarried, hewn and squared for the Lord's building, if I can help it!" John Wesley summed up the Yorkshire Baptists as "a carnal, cavilling, contentious sect always watching to steal our chickens". There seemed no way to suppress the Antinomians — those who had known Darney before he deserted them for Methodism, or who had been in contact with Mary Hepton: finding no way as Methodists, they popped up as General Baptists. The Baptists built a chapel in Haworth itself, and it took Grimshaw some time to get over that shock.

He reacted positively. In Haworth a board of trustees was set up and one day, before the Mad Parson stepped into Heaven,

170

Grimshaw and others were seen walking purposefully to deliberate over a patch of land where Main Street ran out onto the moor. A legacy of one hundred and forty pounds began the preaching house fund and Grimshaw attempted to raise more by gambling in the State Lottery of 1758. More money came from the balance of the accounts at the next quarterly meeting. The building occupied Grimshaw for a year. Methodist preachers who were also masons and carpenters worked without payment on it. Periodically throughout each day they knelt in the roofless building, even when it was raining or snowing, and prayed for funds and for sinners to repent.

At this time a tall, sun-tanned stranger, about thirty years of age, wearing an old soldier's jacket which showed that he had returned from the war in Spain, appeared in Haworth. He stayed at the inn but avoided telling anyone who he was. He spent a lot of time in his room, which was above the public one, and the conversation of the drinkers there would grow silent as they heard the whirring of small machines. This silence in its turn caused the shy stranger to stop whatever he was doing. The maid said that he had bits of clockwork strewn all over the place. Another curious thing about him was that he seemed to know his way about the district. He walked moodily and alone along the streams, where children and shepherds had come upon him building miniature dams, culverts, cataracts and bridges. As soon as he was surprised, he became embarrassed and quickly destroyed his work with his foot.

One evening a group of young men who had time on their hands and money in their pockets got him drunk in order to solve this mystery. The stranger was obviously not normally a drinker and for once he became indiscreet. "My name is Michael Beever. I lived i'Haworth until twelve years ago and I was married to Sally Rushworth who died in the plague, when I went to the the wars and left a child in the cradle."

"That'd be Little Ben Rushworth. We called him after his grandfather — you being away."

"What happened to him?"

"He died in the hospital."

"He didn't, tha knows! He was sent down a coal-pit and died there."

Once sober again, Michael Beever became even less approachable than before, and regretted having spoken. He left his room at the inn and took a remote cottage. But from going to the apothecary's quite

171

often he struck up a noticeably tender acquaintanceship with Ruth Appleyard. He saw in her a woman who although the same age as himself was still slender and beautiful, the lines and sinews showing on her face and throat only when she was tired or distressed — which she seemed to be quite often. She had long legs and a supple waist so that her body moved deliciously. Her hair and eyes were a soft brown colour and this, he felt, was the hue of her inner nature: a colour suggesting not boldness but patience. Her opinions were broader and wiser than he was used to hearing in Haworth, but she expressed them with modesty as if she was aware that her knowledge was limited. He deduced that many men must have fallen in love with her, yet she seemed to respond to him. He detected in her a longing for broader horizons — despite which she was a good housewife, as he saw from her appearance and that of the shop.

"What do you want me for? You're a fine looking man and could woo a younger woman," she teased him.

"Nay, I haven't time for slow wooing. I know from when I was a lad that you are a fine housewife, Mrs Appleyard. That's what I need. I've my schemes to be getting on with. You shall be rich, I promise you, and I think you deserve it. Have you heard of Mr Lombe's silk mills?" No, she hadn't. "All the spinning is done with machines. You 'appen won't have heard either of Mr Lawrence Earnshaw's device for spinning cotton by machine? He made it and then destroyed it because he said it would take bread out of the mouths of the poor. The man was a fool to himself. You can't afford to carry on that way in this life and I mean to continue where Earnshaw left off. He was soft. I mean to be hard." (He didn't *seem* a hard man, Ruth thought.) "But my researches have to be secret and I need a wife who's close."

Back at the apothecary's, Ruth said, "Jonas, your telling folk that you know your sins to be forgiven is making them laugh at us and I'm afraid to put my head out of doors because of your upbraiding of our neighbours. Everyone is laughing at your foolish sayings."

"I do not care what people say. I am determined to reprove anyone that sins in my presence."

Ruth cried a little. "My happiness with you is over. For according to your words I am a child of the Devil and you a child of God. You do not love me as you used to."

"If thou wouldst seek redemption in the blood of Christ we would be ten times happier than before. But if thou wilt not come to

Heaven with me, I will not go to Hell with thee for company."

She began to cry more. "I cannot live with thee!"

Jonas answered after a long pause. "It's time t'expiate our sins." His eyes were narrowed, his smile was fixed with the expression of one who had anticipated this scene and thought carefully what to do about it. "Parson's building a chapel. You can go with yon godless stranger if a contribution is made to the fund."

"How?"

"We'll have a proper auction for you in front of the church."

To point up Ruth's virtue rather than her beauty, on the day of the auction Jonas had her dressed modestly, not as the town apothecary's wife but as if she belonged to a weaver. For a week she had slept separately from her husband, not speaking to him but dutifully preparing his meals. This morning after cleaning her kitchen she stood like a patient beast whilst Jonas wrapped the rope around her neck. With her hair lifted under her cap, she felt the coarse hemp's weight upon her skin. "What wilt tha do for scouring thy pots and crucibles when I'm gone, Jonas?" "The Lord's will be done," he answered.

He closed his shop for the day. Ruth followed him onto the street at ten o'clock in the morning and she blushed before the people gathered to watch her. There wasn't any need for a notice about the sale — a word had only to be dropped at the inn, and the whole township was swallowed into a conspiracy; for although no-one was sure whether the practice was legal or not, divorce was so useful that blind eyes were turned to the facts of the law, and they clung to this parody of an auction. Without looking back at her former home, Ruth walked with her hands folded underneath the droop of rope. Her eyes were turned down upon it but she knew of the attention that she attracted by the ripple of silence that advanced before her, one loom after another stopping its clatter as she came close. She could not disguise her sensual walk, and there were women who expressed their malice, whispering that Ruth had not satisfied her husband.

The couple reached the north wall of the church where there was always some trading taking place. Amongst the pedlars, Ruth stood on a gravestone. Apprentices, young woolcombers and weavers looking for fun had come along with some ale, and they cheered when they saw the Appleyards' arrival. Michael Beever stood apart, smartly dressed as if he had indeed come for a wedding, feeling awkward and not sure what to do with his big hands, but making his presence felt with sharp glances to keep the idlers well behaved. Ruth was not too abashed to stare at him, with a look of desperation, across the faces in between. He shyly switched his glance over the crowd, to the tip of the church tower, and to Jonas' gesticulations as he began the bidding — the movements of his hands almost as if he was playing his lost violin.

"Who will give me one shilling?"

"That's a big price for a cast-off!" someone, hidden, dared to shout.

"It's for t'chapel fund, now!"

"Three shillings," offered a lonely desperate man who took the bidding seriously. "And a good home."

"Nay, it's a poor spot on the dark side of the valley. The snow stays until May and last year it brought the roof down. He's got a temper like sour beer from living up yonder!"

"I've mended it now!"

"Which — your temper or the roof?" Everyone laughed at the old man's seriousness.

"Five shillings," Michael Beever cut across the joking. This brought silence.

"Seven," Jonas said.

"He's sucked all the juice from the fruit and now he wants seven shillings for it!" someone joked.

"It's for the chapel," Jonas said.

"Seven it is," Michael answered, blushing deeply. Jonas stepped down from the gravestone, an invitation for Michael to come forward and clinch the deal. He waded head and shoulders above the crowd that made way for him. The two men each spat on their palms and clasped hands loudly and firmly. The crowd hurrahed. Some music on a whistle began, as if for a wedding, but then the musician became embarrassed and put his instrument away, which brought a few titters and glances towards Sowdens. Ruth dropped the rope from her neck, her attention fixed entirely on her future life. Jonas coiled the rope that had fallen in the grass at his feet and prepared to go to Sowdens with his money. He avoided looking at the lovers, or indeed at any other couple. For a few moments he felt utterly bereft: a sensation that he'd failed to imagine beforehand. As he thought of the irrevocability of what he'd done, his mouth went dry and he could not speak. "Tha's done a bad deal there, Jonas Appleyard," a

174

spectator bluntly told him, and all he could do for answer was to slip off to Sowdens quickly.

Michael Beever did not kiss his bride. He merely touched her fingertips timidly for a second, as if they might burn him. She tried to hold back her sensuality but it flew like electricity into his body, and as they walked away together up the street he avoided brushing against her, as if she was contagious. Ruth felt proud to answer the Haworth folk with this fine young man at her side. Some older women smiled warmly and one bright-eyed crone grasped Ruth's hands, kissed them and said with feeling, "God be with you." They went a long way out of town, passing a waterfall roaring amongst stones and rowan trees. "There's a great waste of power and profit in that, Mrs Appleyard. It's a mortal sin to let God's gifts run to such waste," Beever said. She had passed this place a thousand times before but had never thought or heard it spoken of in this way. Beever took his wife to an isolated cottage with its curtains drawn. Inside it smelled of sawdust and oil. There were lathes, bits of turned wood, brass and clockwork scattered on benches. Out of habit, Ruth began to tidy the litter. When at last their eyes met she said, "My name is Ruth Beever, not Mrs Appleyard," and he kissed her. That night when he entered her she felt as though violins were playing inside her womb.

A short time later, Mercy Rushworth sold leeches to a young woman who needed to fake a hymen. The girl was about to marry and did not dare let her husband know that she had lost her virginity, so Jonas Appleyard had advised her to put leeches to suck inside her opening, leaving them there for a week before her wedding by which time they would have brought up blisters full of blood which would be burst by her husband and deceive him. Mercy went to the apothecary with her barrel of leeches. "Do not look so angry! The price will not always remain low," he said. "With all you poor women collecting them, leeches will become scarce and we apothecaries need a plentiful supply of blood." By the way he looked at her she knew there was something he didn't dare ask her. "What do you want from me?" she asked, for she had reached deep enough into the well of unhappiness to be able to face every truth.

"Could you fetch me women's blood?" he asked, smirking. He spoke rapidly as he saw her anger deepen. "For scientific work. Come and see what discoveries I am making and you may become a great benefactor to it!'' He led her to the back of the house into a room with its curtains drawn. There was a fire that looked as though it was always burning, but water from a spring running out of the flagstones was being allowed to spread over the floor, so that there was a humidity and a smell of fungi that gripped her throat. Mercy saw a row of leather bags suspended from the ceiling and damp at their bottoms. By the side of each one was a jar. ''It is known to science that woman is but the fertile field into which is planted the seed bearing the inheritance of the ages. So it must be possible to imitate the conditions of the womb as a fertile garden and grow mankind in it. These sacks are dampened with women's blood to feed the male seed planted there. Mine and also good Mr Grimshaw's. An ideal father of the ages! I have an arrangement with the workhouse master to obtain blood, but unfortunately nothing grows because the blood of the common women is inferior, weakened by their hard lives, and I cannot induce high-born ladies to participate.''

Mercy picked up a knife. Her cap dropped from her head and her hair bristled. ''Blood! Blood! Blood!'' she screamed as she twisted the knife in Appleyard's stomach, forcing it into him as he collapsed, and she wept beside him on the wet red stones.

One day the woodcutters came to fell the oak trees around Mary Hepton's cottage. John Shread, who lived there with settled upon his face the happy look of one who has received an epiphany, lost his joy when he saw her horror as she dashed out to try and stop the woodcutters. They laughed at her. ''Get off us, you old scarecrow, or thou'lt be hung!'' As the first blow fell upon the oaks, the birds that had been at peace with Mary all flew away. Mary ran back and forth helplessly under the flutter and clatter of pigeons' wings, the quick bright darting of tits and finches. ''Thou'rt an old witch and thou'rt losing thy familiars!'' a woodcutter shouted. Another pointed at Shread. ''Does yon wispy fellow turn into a black cat o'nights?'' An owl, blinded by the light, stumbled like an untidy rag out of the first oak tree to fall. The tender grasses, that had been like a million threads of gold and silver in the glade, were already trampled underfoot. Mary, trembling and white, cowered on the ground. John Shread had today brought her the genitals of a hare to hang above their bed to induce fertility, but Mary could not be consoled. Tomorrow the men would come for more oak trees. They would bring horses to drag them away, leaving nothing but wreckage and a desolate burnt moor. Already their fires of twigs and brushwood were smouldering and smoking through the night. Mary knew that this was the beginning of the end when all the numinous plants and animals of the wood and the moor would be destroyed. The woodcutters came every day and Mary stayed behind closed doors, keeping Shread in with her. Her animals and birds made their exits and entrances through the windows — one morning the woodcutters were amazed to see a litter of young rabbits come hopping over the window sill.

As Mary expected, in a week's time a constable and half a dozen men came with handcuffs and chains. "Mary Hepton! Deposition has been laid by your cousin Robert Greenwood that in November 1746 you did lay curses upon your husband so that he died." She and Shread were led in chains through Heptonstall. The children chanted at her, "Old Mother Hepton is a witch!" Shread was whipped and locked in the stocks for a day. Mary, even though she was ready to die and she "confessed", was "put to the question".

"Did you not give birth to a litter of rabbits, saying to a woodcutter that you had received an immaculate conception from the Queen of Heaven?" As they applied the screws, she confessed and blasphemy was added to the charges. "Have you not tried to raise your own breasts by sucking at them?" She admitted it. "Have you told that Christ would be born again in a weaver's loft in Heptonstall?" Yes. "Have you not requested William Darney to purchase a baby for you at a fair?" After her torture Mary was forced to wear a brank, for fear she would be "noisy" whilst being taken to her hanging. The brank was an iron cage for her head, with one metal band over her shorn hair locking into another around her mouth and chin. The metal over her face had a chain attached so that she could be led by the nose. Where the band passed in front of her mouth, there was a projecting piece of iron two inches long that fitted under her tongue. At its end it had a tiny ball with spikes. The brank was too large for Mary. The iron was too heavy for her head and made it ache. Resigned and broken as she was, she began to quiver again with fear as the jailer, with extra roughness because of his horror at her crime, thrust the terrible spiked bit into her mouth. The natural quivering of her tongue was enough to draw blood, which she swallowed to avoid the humiliation of having it trickle from her lips.

Because her legs were broken in torture, Mary had to be wheeled

177

on a cart to the Halifax gallows. Whilst she was on her way Shread was being pressed into service with other men to beat and burn the woodlands and Mary's cottage, to kill every rabbit they could find lest it turn into an incubus that would impregnate maidens and give birth to devils. Mary was dragged to the top of Beacon Hill where an iron cage waited for her body. On this high skyline she would swing until she rotted. The jolting of her cart sent pains through her body and the crowds, puffing up the hill, laughed as she leapt about like a cat thrown onto a hot stove. Across the sky she saw the crows that would eat her. Blood trickled out of her mouth. When she reached the gallows and they tumbled her about to fit the noose around her neck, she was desperate to speak no matter what pain and blood resulted. "The day will come when you will be rained upon with blood of the Queen of Heaven!" she thought, and tried to say a little of it, her eyes squinting madly through her iron mask. She could not be understood and they laughed at her struggles. Then as they saw her mad eyes in the iron bars and the blood streaming over her white face they themselves turned white and silent, recovering to chant:

> "I would she were well bolted with a bridle,
> That leaves her work to play the clack
> And lets her work stand idle,
> For it serves not for she-ministers,
> Farriers nor spinsters,
> Cobblers nor button-makers,
> To descant on the Bible!"

Unaware that his father now lived secretively in a moorland cottage, with the belief that his son had died in a coal-pit, Ben Rushworth used to go onto those same moors looking for larks' nests and carrying several boxes containing young birds. He had decided to use his talent for capturing them to raise money to build his own chapel, like the great Baptist Dan Taylor. (Taylor had also taught himself to read and write in a coal-pit, at Sourmilk Hall in Halifax; he had been rejected by local Baptists and so had walked to Nottinghamshire in winter to be baptised in the River Idle at Gamston, returning to "steal" a whole Methodist congregation at Wadsworth near Hebden Bridge. There with his own hands and the help of his sect he quarried stone to build a chapel-farmhouse where he also kept a shop for selling farm produce.)

Gangs of men were burning the heather and as the fire advanced towards the larks' nesting areas, Ben ran back and forth trying to stamp it out, as frantic as the birds themselves. At first the men laughed at him, but seeing how seriously he frustrated their work, it led to fights in which of course Ben was defeated. Now he sat under a rock on the fringe of the moor, smarting from his wounds but mostly sad because of problems he was having with the irreligious pitmen. Meanwhile his expert eye studied the habits of the larks nesting safely on the enclosed slopes below the moor. They were singing at a dozen points in the heaven above. The young birds that he had in boxes were thus able to learn their songs and Ben brought them onto the moor for three or four hours a day for this purpose. He would leave the prisoners to listen to their parents singing whilst he went with a specially made wicker basket to where he knew the fledgelings would be ready. When the free larks dropped from the sky, they hoped to deceive by landing several yards away from their nests and running through the grass with their crests lowered. Ben had to keep his eye on where the bird ran to and be able to walk there afterwards, though losing sight of the nest behind walls and in valleys. He needed to capture the young larks at the point when they were ready to fly away. Often he had to remember where nests were after several weeks, and the whole territory sloping below the moor was mapped in Ben's memory with the sites of birds' nests in different stages of readiness for him.

When the larks stopped singing at twilight Ben returned to Denholme. The young man now had his own two-roomed cottage near the pit. It was filled with caged larks and there was a large engraving of the Baptism of Christ. Ben collected memoirs and hymns published by Nonconformists, and also music for the recorder which he played to train the larks to sing. His cottage was a shop for the sale of larks, religious tracts and music, just as Dan Taylor sold farm produce. The miners bought the birds in order to hold competitions in which they gambled on whose lark sang longest and best. The bird, still in its little wooden box, was placed inside a larger cage of open wicker-work which was covered with a sheet, then the whole was set near a window and the bird released from its box. It rose to sing and harmlessly baffle its wings against the sheet which let in diffused light. The colliers recognised subtle qualities of pitch and tone. The lark tunes, especially designed or perhaps evolved since the days of Orpheus, were a mystical secret written in longhand and passed amongst the initiates. Ben through his evangelising was particularly well able to collect tunes as well as larks. He had been enthralled by the lark cult since he first saw men who had climbed wearily out of the earth's bowels, with their grey skins engrained with dust, squatting as if still cramped in a mine in a room filled with tobacco smoke, beer smells and the twitter of captive birds, their attention fixed upon the window where a creature fluttered so fast against the cloth that it seemed to become insubstantial, a throb of electricity giving out waves of such song as would be otherwise unimaginable to earthly people. The colliers would become silent in adoration, allowing not even the chink of a glass placed softly on a table.

"I know how to catch larks!" Ben had said when he was only seven years old.

The miners laughed. "But does tha know how to lay hold of a good one? And what will tha do when tha's caught it?"

"It'll sing for me."

"Not unless tha knows what to do with it, it won't. It's a special art, lad. Find us enough young uns on thee rambles and we'll 'appen show thee."

Today Ben came with mixed feelings off the moor to Denholme. He looked forward to his cottage, with the young birds waiting to be fed and his "Christ's Baptism" on the wall, ale in the cupboard and a spring of fresh water in the yard. But firstly he had to run the gauntlet of the miners who sneered at his religion and were envious of his talent with the larks. The days when they had prayed with him in the mine were past. They now hated him for his strangeness and nobody spoke to him in the pit. It was agony for him to go down there. As he came between the houses, young men shouted after him and threw stones. Ben ran, thoroughly frightened. He turned a corner to his house and saw windows smashed, the window frames and doors burned and a little smoke curling from the bedroom. His heart stopped. His next fear was that they would come for *him* presently. No-one was about except an old woman on a doorstep.

"Who did it?"

"Some young men. They don't expect folks to be different to themselves. It's by keeping close that we survive," she answered shrewdly.

Ben went forward into the smoky damage. Most of his larks had been stolen but some had been burnt in their cages. His furniture and the stairs to his bedroom had been smashed. He tried to clean up some of the mess but he soon grew disheartened and fled. He went to the house where he had first been apprenticed: the old miner was a pious man even if his wife was sour. They took him in and gave him supper. They tried to teach him to be as others were — surely he had now learnt his lesson! — but he could hardly speak to them. He sat with them all evening and then he slept on a bed which they lowered out of the wall. He was awake for a long while, thinking and praying.

The next morning Ben went down the mine, taking as many candles as he could carry. As he was lowered he looked over the shrinking disc of the sky, but he did not see any larks. He had been told that his preaching was as sweet as the singing of a lark and he had longed to build a chapel on the moor amongst the birds. He had once been called "the Orpheus of the Lark Cult". Miners, their women and children did not speak to him. He crawled and wriggled as far along the tunnels as he could, choosing finally a worked-out shaft. All morning he dragged stones to the end of this tunnel. Nobody cared about what he was doing for he was always up to something peculiar, and by midday the miners were joking that he was building a chapel. Ben did not stop to rest. He had brought no food or drink with him and he wasn't offered any. When he had sufficient stones, he built a wall in front of him, and by the end of the afternoon he had walled himself in. He lit another candle and sat in his tomb to read his Bible. Nobody even asked where he had gone to — the few who cared told themselves that he must be walking about the moors as usual.

When his candles guttered out, the boy sat in darkness allowing himself at last the luxury of tears. Meditating and sleeping in short naps he eventually grew too weak to think, whereupon God filled his mind with an ineffable golden light that shone through his darkness. Sometimes he heard voices and other noises beyond the wall. He grew too weak even to stretch; he reached delirium, slept and died.

In the winter of 1762–3, Grimshaw's fifty-third year, the West Riding was locked in deep snow until late spring. The clothiers could not even get their goods to the piece hall, let alone overseas, and Dutch traders did not come much to Yorkshire. The weavers could hardly work at all. Apart from needing unfrozen streams for washing, the making of a single piece required taking it to a fulling mill, bringing it home to be stretched on a tenter frame in the open air, packhorsing it off once more for the nap to be clipped in a cropping shed, and then finally taking it to a main clothier or to the piece hall. What weaving was done was stored for months in barns. If a road was cleared, soon a bitter wind would blow the snow back again. This noise of wind steadily sifting the snow off the drifts and rattling the black icy twigs was almost the only sound on the moors. Food and fuel was scarce and there was no fodder for cattle. Grimshaw led prayers for an end to it. Weavers like John Shread — wrapped in goose fat and in as many layers of clothes and rags as they could bear, or find — grew delirious from starvation, isolation, the monotony and silence of snow.

Shread had found himself a cottage well away from neighbours. For two months a snowdrift lay up to his eaves. When there was a little midday sun, the edges of the drift thawed and re-set in long icicles. A little spring kept bubbling away in a patch of emerald green the size of a handkerchief and surrounded by a jagged lace of glassy icicles: John dreaded this last trickle of life freezing up. The familiar moors around him were thrown into new shapes under the drifts and at night even when it was moonless there was an eerie brightness, with lamps here and there reflected in the snow as in a cloudy lake. It was silent, with birds and animals fled to their holes, coming out sometimes to leave chains of prints over the soft pillows of snow which Shread in agony and frustration wanted to pummel with his fists.

Shread's first sign of the weather changing was when he woke sweating under his rags and blankets, and heard avalanches sliding off his roof with a noise like huge piles of wet cloth falling. The weather grew too warm and damp too quickly. Mist hung in the air, the roads became quagmires. The grass, sickly yellow and like patches of skin from which bandages have been ripped, but nonetheless such a welcome sight, turned into marshlands. It seemed that the water would never drain away even though it was trickling and pouring all the time and causing floods. Before long everyone hated that rattle of water running out of the snowdrifts down the stony roads. Now you could hardly see your way to travel because of the mists.

The manure heaps around Haworth dissolved in this flood water, crept all over town and could not be kept from trickling in at doors. Smells arose again after the frosts. People emerged from the winter thinner, paler and very hungry, and after two weeks the first victim went down with typhoid fever: a man who, having complained of

182

headaches, rushed up the steps out of a woolcomber's shop to be sick in the street. His fellows insisted on examining his body for the rash symptomatic of the fever. It had not yet arrived, but looking at his swollen stomach and remembering how he had been off his food, everyone knew that "the Plague" had returned, as it did to Haworth about once every five years.

When Grimshaw became ill he wrote to John Wesley who advised sea bathing. To leave moorland Yorkshire was impossible for Grimshaw and he gave what he knew would be his last sermon.

"When man was prevailed upon by t'serpent through his wife to eat the forbidden fruit he in that instant lost his life, light, power, innocence and happiness. He became a mere helpless, guilty, miserable mortal. . . . While man is seeking happiness in a thousand preposterous ways his mind is filled by the Devil and by this means he is exposed to the wrath of God, eternal death and damnation. . . . Every sin, however small, even a sinful thought, will expose the soul and the body from the Last Judgement onward to the eternal intolerable wrath of God. The transgressor's whole future life, though inwardly and outwardly as pure as an archangel's, cannot prevent it . . . I am determined to the very end to pull down man, to keep him down and never let him recover so far as his knees till with a broken heart and a contrite spirit the dear Redeemer raises him!"

Grimshaw left his church and its sick people in a huge holy silence. That afternoon he made his last journey — or did he dream this experience by his fireside? As he slopped and slipped across wet moorland, a mist like a damp cloth was woven out of the thawing snow, filling hollows and winding in strands around the headlands. It was warm and muggy, and Grimshaw was in a heavy sweat. In his pain he had to keep resting, but feared to do so because when he paused the terrifying spirit of the moor invaded his senses. He felt demons breathing upon his neck. He tried to control himself but in the end he had to turn, expecting to see raised claws, red eyes and fiery nostrils. His weak eyes and the delirium and sickness made objects dance and waver — the balloons or strands of mist and the black eroded stones the size of chapels. Some were shaped like great pregnant bellies set upon single spindly legs. A hundred yards away a wall of mist pranced and rustled like a tormented beast. Strands of it were torn off and evaporated. Grimshaw went forward with his head down, watching out for snowdrifts and the small deep pools of brown water. When he raised his eyes, a few yards from the mist, the sweat poured from him and his limbs melted as he saw a figure fifteen feet high. It did not move but as William stayed rooted to the spot, so did the monster. Grimshaw, with the itching sweat running like rainwater over his face, struggled to save himself from sinking into the earth, from running — although there was nowhere to run to — from imploring on his knees for mercy, reasoning with himself that the vision was no more than his own shadow thrown upon the mist.

Overcoming this terror, he was faced with another one. Someone was sitting so close by that it was a miracle Grimshaw had not seen him already. William leapt visibly and his heart banged like the hammers in a fulling mill. It was an old man powerful like Grimshaw himself but with a long beard, and he was calmly gnawing on a mutton chop. The grease dribbled upon his lips. Grimshaw felt that although he had never met this bearded old chap before, yet he had known him all his life. The old man beckoned Grimshaw to sit next to him. William humbly accepted, seating himself on a lower stone and shivering now from his congealed sweat. The old fellow calmly gnawed and dribbled over his mutton chop. Grimshaw caught the smell of his breath and felt certain that he was spreading the Plague, but he didn't care.

William asked his name but he merely answered that he was an old trader in wool who had seen many things and would see more. He claimed that he owned everything but would own even more. "I am rich but I am poor . . . and you are the incumbent of Haworth," he said, but of course it did not surprise Grimshaw that a stranger knew this. "God will be worshipped everywhere and yet there will be no God," the old man said and chewed again. A few tears ran from one eye and sped like mercury, repelled by the grease of his beard and his chop. "The land will be burnt until it is barren, poisonous fumes will cloud Heaven and man will choke in his own breath." Later that evening William Grimshaw was found cowering against a stone wall, delirious and shaking, and had to be carried half a mile in a farmer's cart to his bed.

He quickly prepared for his funeral. He wanted "a poor man's burial suit, and about twenty of my spiritual brethren to attend". He was not in church on the following Sunday, and when a stranger took the service, led prayers for the afflicted and spoke of Grimshaw, everyone knew that the parson's last hour had come. "Molly!" William whispered from his black, carved oak bed at

Sowdens. "My sickness is dangerous. Do not let too many come near me." Nonetheless Methodists could not resist sickbeds; the word spread from cottage to piece hall to market and they arrived unsummoned.

William Darney was amongst the first. He came from his farm at Bacup, walking carelessly across the sodden landscape on one of his peddling circuits (which he had taken up again after being expelled from the Methodists) and he thought he might as well visit his old friend at Haworth, also selling a few balsams and prophylactics in the town at the same time. The church bell tolled all day there for the sick and dying. Together with Darney's tread, it echoed down the empty stone funnel of the steep street. His red hair and beard had grown wild and long again, he carried an assortment of bags, and when he called at the inn nobody guessed he could ever have been a preacher or a Methodist. In the public room, where Darney's clothes began instantly to steam before the fire, and where he displayed a variety of livid bottled cures, preventative powders and charms, was a gentleman returned from Sowdens. He was a stranger to the West Riding who was baffling the natives with his enthusiasm for favourably contrasting the "sublime terror" of their mountains with the vice of the cities.

"How is Mr Grimshaw?" Darney interrupted, with obvious deep feeling. The gentleman looked at the Scots pedlar, thinking with amazement that the great preacher of Haworth had apparently reached the heart of even the rudest inhabitant. "Whilst Death points his javelin at his heart, he beholds the face of the King of Terror as if it is the face of an angel."

"Is good Mr Grimshaw suffering?"

"I have rarely seen anyone suffer so." The whole room became silent, for in Haworth they knew what suffering was. "But he thinks only that he will soon be at home for ever with the Lord — a 'poor, miserable sinner, redeemed by His blood', as even he considers himself to be."

"Ah! God be thanked for faith."

The stranger could not be sure whether Darney was sarcastic or not. He answered angrily, "The faith of Mr Grimshaw has put Haworth on the lips of thousands — not owing to some royal personage or merchant prince, but to a great Methodist hero and parson. It is one of those obscure places which, like the fishing towns of Galilee, owe their celebrity to the Gospel. The desert has become a

185

garden of the Lord, producing fruits of righteousness, whilst the barren wilderness has rejoiced and blossomed like the rose."

Darney walked up to Sowdens. He went straight into the kitchen, knowing that only Molly was in charge, and sat down in front of the fire as if the place was an inn, removing his soaked boots and stockings — as before, his clothes had begun to steam when he entered. Molly took offence at those of the Methodists whom she thought made too much of themselves; who visibly tried not to vomit at the revolting smell, the sight of Grimshaw's flushed face and bloodshot eyes, his delirium and pain during the delivery of their eulogies; for she who had been so frail as a girl went uncomplainingly in and out of the sick-room. But the servant-woman liked William Darney. Under his mop of hair he looked tired and worn, she thought.

"Mr Grimshaw will be pleased to see *you*," she said.

"Do you think so?"

"If he knows you. Most of the time he is not himself, poor man. But he is awake now, waiting for God to call."

"There was a pinch-faced gentleman at the inn who said he had been, and who I fancy was more to Mr Grimshaw's taste."

Molly pulled a face. "It was Mr Newton, who is writing a *Life*. I could tell a tale or two to put in their books! The master says himself that if people knew what a heart he has, they would not honour him as they do."

Darney clattered up the uncarpeted stairs. Before Grimshaw's eyes the room was filled with an impression of redness, like a slowly shifting glacier of blood. "The Lord have mercy!" Darney exclaimed in shock at the wreck lying before him.

"William Darney!" As Grimshaw recognised the voice, his emotion was so great that it rendered Darney speechless. He came forward and softly kissed the parson's terrible flesh.

"It was a sad day when you neglected the Lord's business," Grimshaw said.

Darney was silent for a while. "I had a child once who expected to see the Millennium arrive for his next birthday. Now the boy is indeed with the Lord, passed away at Kingswood School without my knowing ought about it until I received the bill for expenses. There was one item for the repair of six pairs of shoes — he took after us for itinerating, I fancy."

186

"You should not be discouraged from persevering with the Lord's business," Grimshaw repeated.

Darney looked misty-eyed through the window where, though it was early April, the trees were still bare, the grass stalks old, stiff and yellow, the heather without signs of life, the enclosures lying under water. "The spring comes late to these parts."

"God's summer is bound to come and you must have faith in it. When I was first in Haworth the churchwardens piled their hats and coats upon the holy table and sat upon it. It is better now."

"I met a woman making her soup from bones that had been rejected by the dogs," Darney said. But Grimshaw had already passed out, through pain that nothing in the pedlar's bag could ease.

A day later, Grimshaw's son John, wrecked by opium and syphilis, came shamefaced into his father's room, hurt with guilt and having little to say. For many years William Grimshaw had imagined his own deathbed when his son would repent. But the youth did not cry. He looked at his father's shrivelled body, hair gone and reduced to a queer reminder of helpless pathetic babyhood, and he felt an inner hollowness at what he thought of as his father's wasted life — John had just visited his friend Thomas Pighells, who was dying in a different style, cursing the fire in his bowels, and having a pair of fighting cocks brought into his bedroom.

"Take care of my horse," was all that William asked of his son.

"Once it carried a saint and now it is to bear a devil," John answered wanly.

William looked steadily at his son for a long while. "Thou'rt a thin wisp of a lad," he said. "I will pray for you as long as I live. And if there be such a thing as praying in Heaven, I will pray for you there also."

Only Molly was present when William died. "Oh Molly!" he whispered. "I have suffered this night like the blessed martyrs. My flesh has been roasting before a hot fire."

"Lord, you look burnt in an oven."

"But I have nothing to do now but step out of bed into Heaven. I have my foot on the threshold already."

William's coffin was carried by horse litter to Ewood, a long procession winding over the hills behind it. He was finally taken to Luddenden to be buried next to Sarah in their common grave.

Epilogue

"A FEW SUCH as he would make a nation tremble. He carries fire wherever he goes," John Wesley had said of Grimshaw. Yorkshire did tremble after him and it was assuaged by building "preaching houses" — later called chapels. John Wesley fulfilled his dream of erecting one at his favourite hilltop site of Heptonstall. The complicated, octagonal oak roof was made in Rotherham fifty miles away, and the sections brought on packhorses along the Pennines; through Luddenden, past Ewood and Dan Taylor's Baptist Chapel at Hebden Bridge, and up the steep road to Heptonstall. People lined the route singing hymns, waving branches of flowering hawthorn and throwing petals before the horses. Within a hundred years every community had a chapel, usually founded by a tradesman whom Grimshaw, during his storming through the West Riding, had "awakened" to the fact that he would grow prosperous with Methodism. The congregations often filled the new churches before they were completed. At Colne, the weight of people caused the balcony beams to be pulled out of the walls and the crowd was flung into heaps of quicklime still on the chapel floor. Some were suffocated, others escaped with broken arms, legs, hips, and with quicklime burning their eyes and mouths. Many of them were poor people who were a long way from home and could not afford doctors, but Mr Wesley led them into an adjoining meadow and quietly declared the counsel of God. Grimshaw's greatest memorial was this sprouting of chapels on the crests of the villages, where the hymning within was matched, as Little Ben Rushworth had wished, by the singing of the larks outside, amongst the wild moorland grass that was their nesting place.

When Michael Beever, like other mill-owners, realised that spinning mills by the river and Methodism aloft made excellent partners he became a soldier for Christ, paid for a chapel, placed the largest Bible he could purchase at the workers' entrance to his factory and promoted only Methodists as supervisors, with a first duty to turn

188

one page of the Bible every day. In Methodist churches and class meetings the North of England was first in the world to learn spiritual and material account-keeping, mensuration, obedience and sobriety — skills for both the factory and for socialism. Outside chapel, something of the great preachers' visions was projected onto the landscape: a black charred Hellish scene, with the terrifying fires that had burned so clearly in their minds, now burning in the furnaces of the valley factories where work had become a monotonous punishment for sin. The landscape was cleared of its original spiritual associations in readiness for this violence to be done to it by industrialists. There was no longer anything numinous to restrain men from abusing it. Those who had lived here treasuring and revering the landscape for centuries, now behaved towards it as in the past it had been treated only by invading enemies: a dreadful scarring with fire, pick and spade, whilst they plundered, burned and destroyed in order to find its wealth quickly, quickly, quickly.

Despite the growth of Grimshaw's cause, in Haworth his death left a vacuum. Because of the quarrels between the church trustees and the Vicar of Bradford, the next few "perpetual curates" were quite temporary. The least successful was the Reverend Samuel Redhead, who survived for only three weeks. During his first service the congregation rhythmically stamped their clogs just as they had done for Grimshaw, but this time they left the church before Redhead got to his sermon. On the following Sunday, halfway through the service, an idiot boy who had been set head-to-tail on a donkey and with as many hats as possible piled upon his head, was driven down the aisle and round the church. On the next Sunday Redhead appeared with half a dozen tough-looking strangers from Bradford, who put up their horses at the inn and went into the service. This time there was a drunken chimney-sweep who had been bribed to clean chimneys that morning and come into the church as black as possible. He stood before the pulpit nodding his messy head at everything Redhead said. At last he climbed the pulpit steps, put his arms around Redhead and kissed him. The preacher fled but his henchmen could not prevent his having the sweep's soot-bag emptied over him in the churchyard. Eventually he reached sanctuary at the inn whilst the crowd raged for an hour outside the locked doors and windows.

Patrick Brontë and his family arrived the following week. In

189

the same fashion as Grimshaw's arrival in Haworth, they came
with laden carts struggling up the steep street, everyone watching
wondering what sort of parson this one would turn out to be and
knocking on the firebacks to tell neighbours to come out of doors.
Immediately Brontë established a sick room for his wife Maria in the
new big parsonage by the church. Maria died within a year and her
two eldest children, Maria and Elizabeth, went within a month of
each other, four years later. For the remaining Brontë children life
meant a declension through sickness and fantasies, meanwhile
shooting off electric sparks of vivid life, like lit marsh gas on the
surface of a bog. They consumed their sensual responses greedily
before death claimed them, and their poetical senses gripped what
time or even a maiden's hands would destroy: flowers, a sunny
autumn day amongst the heather, and transient life. They wrote
fantasies together in minute handwriting in tiny books. Emily, particularly, grew up obsessed by the spirit of the moors, pining for
them if she was but a few weeks away, and she searched for their
personification in her father's bizarre predecessor William Grimshaw. There was a portrait of him in the Parsonage and she took all
she could from looking at it. Thinking of him often — for who did
not in Haworth? — she dwelled upon his power, as of a natural
force, and his devotion to his first wife with whom he was re-united
in death.

Her sister Charlotte said of Emily that she "had scarcely more
practical knowledge of the peasantry amongst whom she lived, than
a nun has of the country people who sometimes pass her gates". But
one day when they were young girls they went to see a man who was
supposed to be over a hundred years old, who had taken to his bed
and never left it since many decades previously when the woman
whom he loved had been executed as a witch. His name was John
Shread. Emily led the way. Charlotte, small, dumpy and so short-
sighted that she found her path almost by radar like a bat, had to
struggle behind. They found Shread to be cheerful, garrulous, white,
bearded and smelly. His daughter who was a widow from the plague
looked after him, although she seemed almost as old as her father —
she must have been nearly ninety. On a table near Shread's bed was a
scold's brank which antiquarians had asked him to sell them, but he
wouldn't part with it. He told the Brontë girls that he had lived to a

190

great age because he had always drunk from the right spring. Through his window could be seen Michael Beever's huge mill, where the lights burned all night under the clock tower. Shread told the girls that Beever had devoted his life to making money and machines after he came back from the Spanish War, searched for his son and found that the poor lad had walled himself into a coal-pit. Parties of ladies and gentlemen used to come just to look at the mill, finding it a picturesque item in their tour of iron foundries, water-falls and manufactories. Right next to it was the big house queened over by Ruth Beever with more than thirty servants. No-one born in the district found the mill picturesque. It was full of distressed women, paupers and children, for skill was not needed there and Michael dismissed clever workmen because they tended also to cause trouble. Agents collected children from workhouses all over England to bring them to the isolated valleys of the north where they were legally bound to serve as "apprentices" in the thousands of mills suddenly built after Richard Arkwright lost his patents on his spinning machines. In the apprentice house of Michael Beever's factory the first thing that the boys and girls were shown was a whip hanging on the wall. "Dusta know what that is?" "A whip, sir." "Aye, a whip. That belonged to the old parson. Tha wouldn't know about him, but he brought civilisation to these parts. Tha'll be taught to respect yon whip."

There were heaps of rubbish around the mill and coal smoke drifted from tall chimneys. The grasses on the moors had a coating of soot and when the girls and boys, who had returned to courting there after the death of Grimshaw, ran their fingers upon a blade of grass or heather, they were marked by two black lines. The smoke polluted the old man's bedroom. Tears ran from his eyes. "There were fairies down in that valley when I were a lad, but the Methodists killed them," he said. "Now everyone in Yorkshire's either an evangelist or a backslider." The squeaky old man with the halo of white hair picked up a Bible that looked as though chickens had once been roosting on it, and he quoted chapter 34 from the Book of Isaiah:

For it is the day of the Lord's vengeance, and the year of recom-
penses for the controversy of Zion. And the streams thereof shall
be turned into pitch, and the dust therof into brimstone, and the

191

land thereof shall become burning pitch. It shall not be quenched night nor day; the smoke thereof shall go up for ever: from generation to generation it shall lie waste; none shall pass through it for ever and ever. . . . and he shall stretch out upon it the line of confusion, and the stones of emptiness.